Today's Changing Society
A Challenge to Individual Identity

Edited by

Clarence C. Walton, Ph.D.
Dean, School of General Studies
Columbia University

A Report of an Arden House Conference held November 27-29, 1966. Jointly sponsored by the Graduate School of Business and the School of General Studies of Columbia University, and the Institute of Life Insurance.

INSTITUTE OF LIFE INSURANCE
277 Park Avenue
New York, New York 10017

Contributors

RENÉ J. DUBOS, Ph.D.
Professor
The Rockefeller University

JOSÉ M. R. DELGADO, M.D.
Department of Physiology
Yale University School of Medicine

RABBI ABRAHAM J. HESCHEL, Ph.D.
Professor of Jewish Ethics and Mysticism
The Jewish Theological Seminary

KENNETH E. BOULDING, Ph.D.
Professor of Economics
University of Michigan

AUGUST HECKSCHER
Director
The Twentieth Century Fund

RICHARD N. GOODWIN
Fellow, Center for Advanced Studies
Wesleyan University

BARBARA WARD
Author, Lecturer, Writer

Preface

The tremendous transitions that have swept contemporary society, especially since the end of World War II, have been chronicled and catalogued so extensively that the word "change" itself has become an overworked cliché — a kind of conversation piece which provides common ground for exchange between the sophisticated expert and the partially informed layman. Yet the identification and recording of specific changes are not the same as an examination into the meanings and implications which result from the cumulative effect of such transitions. Here the inquiry is nowhere near the point of exhaustion. Consider these questions: Has technology turned man into a servant for the machine? Has urbanism spawned spires which imprison rather than ennoble the city dweller? Has biological research reduced man to an animalistic plaything of science?

Some people answer the foregoing questions readily in the affirmative. The invasions of privacy, the alienation of youth, the theatre of the ridiculous, the vulgarities of advertising are cited, among other manifestations, as proofs positive of the low estate to which modern man has fallen. Greed for that tempting apple from the knowledge tree has been the cause of his banishment from Eden. Yet others take a different view. The machine, by lifting the burden of wearying work from the back of man, affords him more leisure and, hence, more opportunity to become truly human. The city is hospice to creative artists and interested amateurs. Research has reduced disease, expanded man's years, conquered old terrors like polio, fevers, and tuberculosis.

Much can be said for both sides of the debate. The trouble, however, is awareness that fact and fiction are so intertwined in the arguments and answers that it is difficult to reach a truly rational conclusion. Perhaps the discourse is destined to be endless. Yet we rest with the sure knowledge that men who hold responsible positions are expected to exercise power responsibly. It is precisely for this reason that the Institute of Life Insurance has joined with the Graduate School of Business and the School of General Studies at Columbia University to sponsor a second Arden House Conference (November, 1966) to probe into the meaning of change in terms of its challenge to individual identity. To give focus to the inquiries, three basic questions were asked:

(1) What are we learning from research in the life sciences which has portentious meaning for the *human being?*

(2) What are we learning from the recent studies in the social and moral sciences that have profound significance to man's eternal quest for *being human?*

(3) Do contemporary changes in the environment (and particularly in the urban and political milieu) diminish or enhance man's capacity for behaving humanly?

The first question has been handled perceptively by Professor René Dubos of the Rockefeller University and Professor José Delgado of the Yale University Medical School and their responses have enormous practical relevances. To deal with the second question, the conferees had the privilege of listening to Rabbi Abraham Heschel of the Jewish Theological Seminary and Professor Kenneth Boulding of the University of Michigan. A beautiful intellectual

5

symmetry emerges for the careful reader who takes sufficient time to ponder the relationships developed by the theologian's emphasis on the uniqueness of the individual and the economist's stress on social mechanisms which bind man to man. The Heschel-Boulding syndrome is a gold mine of fascinating insights.

Environmental factors which relate to the third question were handled with remarkable insights by August Heckscher, Director of the Twentieth Century Fund and Commissioner of Parks in New York City, and by Richard Goodwin, formerly special consultant to Presidents Kennedy and Johnson and now a member of the Institute for Advanced Studies at Wesleyan University.

After each "set" of formal talks the conferees broke into small groups, there to engage in intensive discussions relating to the papers that had been presented. The summations of these groups have been prepared by Professors Harry Woolf of The Johns Hopkins University, Douglas McGee of Bowdoin and James Wiggins of Converse College. Finally it should be noted that the conference itself concentrated on domestic issues related to the changing environment — a concentration rendered essential by the relatively short time-span for the meetings. In preparing for its annual meeting the Institute of Life Insurance, therefore, properly took note of the international dimensions by inviting Barbara Ward to speak to the problems of internationalism in terms of tomorrow's world. The intrinsic quality of her speech, plus its relevance to the Arden House Conference which immediately preceded it, suggested the wisdom of incorporating Miss Ward's remarks into this report.

While these papers obviously reveal the quality of the themes and the nature of the dimensions, they cannot of themselves catch the flavor and spirit of this meeting. These can only be suggested through a retrospective glance to the first Arden House Conference which was convened five years ago. The format was designed to bring together the foremost decision-makers of the industry not simply as a closed group of professionals to talk shop; rather the life insurance executives met with an equal number of distinguished scholars in a three-day intellectual dialogue designed to probe certain questions of enduring importance to man and to society at large.

The same structure was employed in 1966 with equally satisfying results. Not once were bread-and-butter problems as such emphasized or discussed; not once did the dialogues focus on the profit picture or tax problems or incentive plans or agency management; not once did trade jargon jar the formal conferences or informal table talks. In short, thirty-two busy chief executives broke from hectic rounds of regular activities to spend three days for thinking and talking with scholars on these most meaningful questions: What changes have come to society? What are we learning about man's physical nature? What can we learn about man's metaphysical essence? Heady questions invite intoxicating answers. One need only note initially that not all the questions appeared equally important to all participants nor were all the "answers" equally satisfactory. Yet the learning process was so evident that there is grounds for confidence that both the men of action and the men of speculation left Arden House better armed to discharge their obligations more responsibly and to use their knowledge more effectively.

Dean Courtney C. Brown of the Graduate School of Business was most helpful in the planning stages of the Conference. The Conference benefited greatly from the expertise of Hoke S. Simpson, who is a master at staging and conducting a meeting of this type. Mr. Byron K. Elliott, Chairman, Board of Directors of the Institute of Life Insurance at the time of the Conference, gave both leadership and inspiration to those present.

CLARENCE C. WALTON
Dean, School of General Studies
Columbia University

Spring, 1967

7

Contents

CHAPTER 1

Defining the Challenge

Clarence C. Walton

**Dean of Columbia University's
School of General Studies**

Because he is a many-splendored creature, man becomes involved in a wide spectrum of relationships: to himself, to his family, to the physical world. It may be suggested, however, that of these many contacts man's relationship to his community represents the eternal problem which provokes a never-ending debate over the appropriate priorities and values to be assigned to individual freedom and to constraints required by the social order respectively. There has been, is, and always will be profound interest by man in the essence of his own nature and in the meaning of the societies he builds and modifies — and sometimes even destroys.

Because of the enduring timeliness of these subjects it has invariably been the case that the representative institution of a given society was the one to encourage serious explorations into the man-society syndrome providing mechanisms whereby such discussions could fruitfully take place. Examples come quickly to mind. As the major entity of a medieval society the Church fostered the practice of retreats so that its members could set aside everyday chores, at least once a year, to ponder systematically the important questions: What is the cosmos? What am I? Who am I? When the University became the prestigious institution of the modern world it established the principle of sabbaticals so that professors could retreat from teaching assignments to renew insights, sharpen perspectives, and then return to the classroom reinvigorated and freshly inspired. Incidentally, the

11

process and the practice have been extolled and updated by John Gardiner in his widely read book, *Self Renewal*.

Now that the large corporation has become a representative organization of contemporary industrial society it is not surprising to find practices akin to retreats and sabbaticals spreading among many business firms. Naturally enough, insurance companies have become acutely sensitive to the need and value of such intellectual undertakings and this second Arden House Conference is the fruit of such sensitivity. Gathered here are men of action and men of reflection to engage in dialogue on meaningful issues related to man's being and man's potential for being human. In some respects the colloquy we are about to launch seems to be an anomoly, if for no other reason than the fact that a persistent strain in western society — the hostility between businessmen and other elites — has seemingly intensified in our times. As Bertrand de Jouvenel has aptly said, "the world of business is, to the intellectual, one in which the values are wrong, the motivations low, the rewards misaddressed." The observation appears to be no exaggeration if one recognizes that of some sixty novels written about the American businessman before the end of the nineteenth century at least fifty were highly critical of the executive. Today the scholar has replaced the novelist and in scholarly circles, the man who, above all others, appeared to the rest of the world as the authentic voice of American sociology, C. Wright Mills, inveighed against executives. To him the managers of large corporations have captured technological innovation, scattered wealth, capitalized the future, debased values.

Yet if there are many who fear the businessman because he is too active, too aggressive, too powerful, and too rich there are others who deride him because he is, literally, too "washed out." In her *History of the Businessman*, Miriam Beard noted laconically that the sheer energy required to organize activities and to calculate profits and risks has a debilitating effect. "No other profession, apparently, equals business in its power to wear a man out. Certainly there was no such generic term as the Tired Soldier. Politicians lived to a great age. Priests flourished on a meager diet and flagellation. Farmers bore toil and misfortune, growing stronger. Only the effort to organize and calculate has brought forth that strange phenomenon, the Tired Businessman!"

Whether endowed with an over-active or under-active thyroid, the businessman inevitably winds up the object of some scorn. Yet historically he was able to maintain a certain kind of durable serenity because he felt "justified." John Calvin provided a theological justification for mercantile pursuits and Adam Smith provided a philosophical apologia for the merchantmen. Thus the businessman could always legitimize his activities either in terms of doing good for God or doing good for man — and, ideally, for both. Yet the legitimacy which came from Providence or from Property has been rudely challenged in a society which whispers that "God is dead" and which knows that managers manipulate property they no longer own.

Faced by a continuance of a certain brand of hostility from intellectuals and denied claim to legitimacy based on property rights, today's executive knows, nevertheless, that the country's material well-being depends largely on the efficacy of his efforts, that the nation's goals and values are unreachable without his positive contributions, that the broad powers which are his are likely neither to be accepted willingly nor discharged effectively even by those who are his strongest critics! So he moves to fulfill important functions in a pluralistic free society with the acute awareness that the categorical imperative from the past (namely, the efficient production of goods and services) has been replaced by a moral imperative to foster a climate of work where the creative energies of man can find release and expression. He is, in short, helped enormously by machines and gadgets to meet society's expectations for production, yet he is hindered by lack of knowledge in those areas where help is most needed: in his dealings with men who are organized in all sorts of ways!

The life insurance companies represented here reflect organizations of vast resources. They have been dedicated to a simple proposition: that financial responsibility for the self and for one's family are good things. Yet is it not apparent that responsibilities for employee's personal growth, for the quality of urban life, for the essential values of a democratic society, for peace among nations have also attached themselves to the large insurance enterprise in ways and in fashions undreamed of by the early founders of this profession?

13

Man himself is changing. The physical environment is changing. The large-scale organization is changing. The city is changing. The nation is changing. The international society is changing. Growing evidence reinforces the premise — urged forcefully upon us by Teilhard de Chardin — that knowledge of evolution may be the beginning of wisdom regarding the destiny of man through change. In this context, therefore, the intellectual probings that are about to be undertaken and the moral soundings that must be made take on a most serious quality. We seem to share a certain foreboding that an American dream of a society built to serve the individual is in danger of reversing the relationship to a point where the individual is to be made to the image and likeness of a machine, or an organization, or a statistical cipher, or a manipulative animal, or a pawn in a political chess game. Challenged by new developments are the importance of work, the excitement of personal creativity, the joy of learning and the delights of leisure. It proves important and instructive, therefore, to examine such new developments in urbanism, science and technology, and politics in order to discern the magnitude of change and its implications for man.

If we turn to social forces first, two pithy observations may be made of modern man: (1) he rushes to be saved by technology and then rushes to be saved from it, and (2) he flees to the city to work and flees from it to live. Americans give the impression of being front-runners in both events. Because commerce has historically been linked to the urban society and because industry has historically exploited technology most effectively, the importance of the foregoing observations to business executives is obvious. A look at the phenomena of modern urbanism and of technology is rewarding.

Urbanism

The migration of men from countryside to city has been one of the major developments of history. His heart may yearn for some garden of Eden but his mind tells him that the asphalt world brings quicker rewards. But is the price of city life too high? At this Conference two points of view may be worth exploring as these relate to (a) the extent of urbanization and (b) the models

14

to guide future city reorganization. The former may be examined first in terms of the magnitude of the urbanization trend.

In his special message to Congress on March 2, 1966 President Johnson declared that "the 70 percent of our population (135 million Americans) now living in urban areas is simply prelude to the coming day, less than a half-century away, when 320 million of the 400 million Americans will live in such areas." The President noted that "during the next fifteen years, thirty million people will be added to our cities — equivalent to the combined populations of New York, Chicago, Los Angeles, Philadelphia, Detroit and Baltimore. Each year, in the coming generations we will add the equivalent of fifteen cities of 200,000 each." The conclusion seems incontrovertible: We are a nation of cities! Yet some experts urge caution by pointing out that the 1960 population distribution, by city size, reveals that 58.3 percent of the nation's total population *lived in rural areas or in cities under 50,000 people, and that only 9.8 percent lived in cities with over a million people.*[1] Despite the caveat, however, we know that cities are growing enormously, are congested, are pockmarked by slums, are tortured by traffic snarls, are claimants on Federal support in the future as farmers were in the past.

How then shall the cities be revitalized and reconstructed? Responses thus far suggest that models for blueprinting future urban patterns are coming from two different sources. European standards (set by Florence, Rome or Paris) indicate that cities can tolerate large population densities so long as each unit is made an almost self-contained center for shopping and enjoyment, recreation and education. It is argued here that the American City is the product of ancient Greece and Rome and of modern Europe. It must become like them — a *Civitas,* or center, for political and economic leadership and a symbol of cosmopolitanism and sophistication. Americans should be proud to be New Yorkers or Chicagoans or Philadelphians as our forebears were proud to be Atheneans or Florentines or Parisians.

Contrasted to this ideal is the picture of the American City as having its true prototype in the Israelite pattern described in the Bible and befitting a people who prize agrarian values. Like the cities of ancient Israel, the American City is said to be located within territorial and political jurisdictions that take precedence

15

over it — in its case, the state rather than the tribe, and in both cases, the nation above that. Thus, the city in America, as in ancient Israel, has developed, not as the equivalent of the state but rather to serve certain specific functions for a pre-existing civil order. The city, therefore, has a *secondary* role to play politically and perhaps a primary role to play socially and commercially.

Daniel Elazar has stressed this point and has insisted that "unlike the classical city which, in effect, first established its limits, and then developed its various functions within those limits, the American and Biblical cities grew almost haphazardously from a central point, the tower in Biblical parlance. In the ancient Biblical city the tower was often a fortress, a temple, or perhaps a grainery which attracted people who did not seek the city per se, but settled around it to make use of the special facilities it offered."[2] The City in our country developed economically through a relationship with the hinterlands and any attempts to centralize marketing or to emphasize the gates of the city are drawing us to an ideal megalopolis as a self-contained unit that will not be realized because it is alien to our basic interests.

Yet August Heckscher hastened to challenge the Elazar thesis. He has already, in previous writings, spoken eloquently of the need to look forward, not backward, and has said that the future of America is linked inextricably to the city.[3] The summons is to lift the city from its present sprawling, disorganized and often tasteless design to a point where we can duplicate and surpass the best in the European traditions. While many of the urban problems are technical in nature (pollution, traffic snarls, location of markets and the like) the question invariably turns to a larger matter where aesthetics and ethics are involved: how shall the city serve the individual? The answer will, of course, be greatly influenced by the choice of model — European or Biblical — that Americans accept as the valid expression of their needs.[4] Should industries build apartments close to corporate headquarters for the convenience of employee and employer? Or will men seek the green pastures of suburbia? Must municipal government be centralized or fractionated?

If the debate over whether our cities dehumanize men rages intensely, the arguments over the impact of technology on man

16

go on no less spiritedly. All the talk over the meaning of our allegedly computerized society or of automation suggests that the issue is a lively one — and will continue to remain so for some time. A few distinctions are worth recording before we raise the question: are science and technology menaces to man?

Are Science and Technology Really One and the Same?

At a time when even knowledgeable people speak of science and technology in the same breath it is well to remember that technological advances made by industrialists during the eighteenth century were *not* dependent on pure science. The steam engine came a hundred years before the theory of dynamics which explained it; advances in the textile industry similarly owed little to pure science; indeed the entire range of inventions that provided the basis for the industrial revolution — the steam engine, the loom, the lathe — were invented by practical men and based upon observation and common sense. Jerome Weisner has observed:

> . . . it was not until the middle of the nineteenth century that extensive practical use was made of the accumulating scientific knowledge. Only then did men begin to exploit the available knowledge of chemistry and electricity for useful purposes. Chemists learned to synthesize organic materials and set up research laboratories for obtaining the new knowledge required to meet their applied objectives. It was in the field of chemistry that research methods were first applied in a systematic manner to develop new products. The application of electricity was more haphazard in the beginning. The scientific observations of Gilbert, Henry, and Maxwell were seized upon by the inventors of the electric motor, the electric generator, the telegraph, telephone, and other devices. Not until the end of the nineteenth century were research methods applied to the exploitation of electrical phenomena, first by Thomas Edison who, in reality, was more of an inventor than a scientist, and later by many technologists in the laboratories of such industries as the General Electric Company and the predecessors of the American Telephone and Telegraph Company. Thus, it was in these fields — chemistry and electricity — that the merger of scientific inquiry and

17

technology first occurred, that the power of the scientific methods was applied to solving useful problems, and that the great value of the thorough understanding of physical phenomena was demonstrated.[4]

The wedding between science and technology has been so phenomenally successful that we tend to forget the separate identities of the married couple. Our forgetfulness blinds us to two very important lessons that are derived from the biography of science itself. The first item of importance is the fact that science, *as a social institution* (namely, a system wherein scientists become important elements in the ordinary life of people and wherein their criteria become the exclusive forms of truth) came into being in the nineteenth century precisely at the time that technology became dependent upon it. The fruits of that dependence are for all to behold: the gains are too dramatic and too measurable to be challenged.

What does concern many sensitive people, however, is the fact that the social institution of science is premised on beliefs that may become harmful to man. Jacques Barzun, for one, has expressed the view that the assumption of purposelessness by science is secreting into society something akin to a poison bottled in various brands of existentialism, in the philosophy of the absurd, and in the notion that man reacts automatically to his environment and does not respond creatively to it. The chief method of science is analysis. This means the breaking down "or cutting up experience for minute study leading to the formulation of relationship" which results in the disappearance of the individual who subsequently reveals himself only — and pathetically — "as a statistical unit shorn of his unique features."[5]

Perhaps corporations have been over-blamed by being singled out for special criticism of their alleged tendencies to shrink the individual into an organizational mold. Blue-collar workers have felt that dehumanizing effects of conveyor belts, and white-collar managers have felt the stings of being called derisively "organizational men." Now we are being told that science has surpassed business in its tendency and in its ability to deny individuality to man. Certainly corporations have moved to a new level of challenge. No longer is sole concern directed to increased efficiency for increased productivity. Of central importance to business leadership is recognition of its capacity to elevate work from chore to challenge, from menialness to meaningfulness, from something scorned to something sought. Practically speaking, insurance leaders face a historic opportunity to revitalize training programs — now often deadly — and into which millions upon millions are poured annually, to end "facade" delegation of authority which allocates unimportant tasks to subordinates under the guise of greater responsibility, to develop rules of accountability formulated by superiors *and* affected subordinates. The job is to take technology and, through it, extend and expand man's capacity for production and for personal satisfaction.

The second lesson of importance, if the individual is to be helped, is best discovered by a rapid look at two important strands in the development of science. While the exact date of its beginning is arguable, it is fair to suggest that Galileo Galilei's birth in 1564 was prelude to momentous developments. With his first revolutionary telescope (which had roughly the power of modern opera glasses) Galileo lifted man's vision from almost blind wonder of the firmament to a probing understanding of space. He was able to show that the moon had a slightly rough surface instead of a smooth one; he was able to detect spots on the sun; to break the Milky Way (until then considered to be a homogenous mass) into individual stars. Within the next few years after Galileo's work, more striking astronomical discoveries flowed than had been made in all the centuries before.

Yet roughly three hundred years were to elapse before an equally startling advance was made in our understanding of living matter. It came on a cold and snowy night in February 1865 when Gregor Mendel read the first part of a paper before an indifferent audience in Brunn to report eleven years of work on the breeding of peas. Mendel's second paper outlined the concept of unit factors of inheritance, the genes, persisting in diverse crosses, recoverable from them, sometimes more enduring than mountains, yet radically altering in an instant on other occasions. Today these atoms of genetics are as familiar as the physical atoms of Dalton.[6]

Note a certain symbolism in these developments. Man's spectacular thrust forward in understanding inanimate nature long preceded his movement toward understanding living matter. He looked outward before looking inward. It is only within the past few years that the explorations into the nature of living beings has taken on such a spectacular turn that one is emboldened to believe that more understanding will come regarding the physical nature of man within the next five decades than has occurred in the last five centuries. In such a perspective it was only natural that the conferees should seek enlightenment on the tremendous advances being made, especially in biology.

The Biological Meaning: What Is Man?

Inquiry into the "whatness" of man will be led by René Dubos of the Rockefeller Institute, and by José Delgado of Yale. The former has already pointed out in previous scholarly papers how science has profoundly induced in man a sense of the importance of change. In times past men saw natural events repeat themselves so regularly and endlessly (in the rising and setting of the sun, in the changing of seasons, in the life cycles of man himself) that he extrapolated these natural cycles to human affairs. Man emphasized the myth of *eternal return,* that is, the idea that present conditions were but one stage in the endless ebb and flow of events. The view was fatalistic in many respects whereas the contemporary mood is a paradox: seemingly we can change everything for the better — except man himself.

Now the scientists are seeking to correct the exception. It was only in the 1950's that scientists began to enlarge on the findings of a young biochemist named Miescher who followed Mendel. It was Miescher who determined that, though enzymes could break down proteins in the outer cell, the contents of the nucleus remained basically intact. This nuclein was an acid with a huge threadlike molecule which breaks into a number of similar fragments when chemically treated. It received the name of Doxyribonucleic acid or DNA. In the last decade or so, men like Linus Pauling and Robert Corey — followed later by Crick, Watson and Wilkins — were able to show that DNA strands from the cells in the body of a single man, if uncoiled, might well span the solar system. The real lesson, of course, was this tremendous capacity for variety in the modes of genetic coding and control.

René Dubos will report on some of his own experiments which suggest two important conclusions: (1) the fact that man seems to be using only five percent of his genetic potential and (2) that the basic response patterns of an individual to environment occur very early in life and are probably unchangeably established by the age of eight. The importance of the early environment (including early schooling) cannot be overstressed.

The concern with the physiological aspects of man's nature lead to some far-ranging observations. Think of the possibilities and problems! If lower animals can regenerate parts of their bodies can we learn enough to enable man to grow a lost finger? Regain sexual vigor after age fifty? Improve brain functioning so much that learning will be easier and memories more retentive? Anyone familiar with the recent experimental work on the brain carried out by José Delgado, who will soon report to us, must surely share in the fruit of much careful work of enormous intellectual and practical significance. Incidentally, this quickening interest in the operations of the human brain is reflected in the fact that in 1964 the Vatican organized, through its Pontifical Academy of Sciences, a symposium where experts delivered scholarly papers on important mentalistic concepts — awareness, attention, thinking, feeling, decision-making, voluntary action and the like. The relationships of consciousness to conscience, of induced reactions to the existence of free will and other relationships have obviously great instructive value to all of us.

Two eminent biologists, Lord Brain and C. H. Waddington, suggested possibilities for making the human memory more efficient and human learning more effective.[8] The latter suggested that by 1984 we may be producing our food in factories, without animals or plants, because we shall then be able to exploit the most far-reaching biological discovery of the last few years, namely the synthesis of proteins in a cell-free system: "Eventually we should be able to manufacture satisfactory food-stuffs in great chemical plants, where masses of ribosomes would be supplied with synthetic amino acids and long-lived messengers — RNA's — with energy-yielding phosphates produced by irradiating chloroplasts with laser-tuned light of the most effective wave length. But that technological dream is nearer fifty than twenty years ahead unless resources are put into these lines of research at something like the level that was used to develop the atom bomb."[9]

If science gives us drugs which permit man to avoid and renounce discomforts, anxieties and challenges in the most delightful kind of hedonistic world, has man enlarged the meaning of human nature? Or diminished himself? How much of a man's brain can we tamper with through drugs, surgery and electronic programming? As population increases will we have to exert tremendous parsimony in the use of nature's resources and in the use of population control? Kenneth Boulding, one of the participants, suggested on another occasion that procreation, historically viewed as an essentially private matter, must now come under public control and that there be established a system of marketable licenses to have children. Boulding quickly adds that as the father of five children himself he does not look forward to the future with equanimity but that the future is dictating a world where an average of two surviving children per couple must be the rule — and no nonsense about it![10]

Man seems to be caught in the eternal dilemma that solutions to one riddle generate other problems. With over two-thirds of the world on a poverty level of subsistence, biologists are able to tell us clearly that malnutrition — itself related to economic limitations and unwise social practices — is responsible for a very large percentage of the disease problems of the world. Control of diarrheal diseases, for example, may come less from prophylactic and therapeutic measures and more from general dietary improvements, from better practices in infant feeding and handling, and through an abundant supply of good water. But even as we move to provide these necessities we become painfully aware that civilization itself brings its own diseases. René Dubos has pointed out that, contrary to general belief, life expectation past forty-five has not increased significantly anywhere in the world. Vascular diseases, chronic ailments of the respiratory tract and certain kinds of cancers are becoming increasingly frequent among the adults of the affluent society. And since industrialization and urbanization are showing signs of becoming universal phenomena these environmental diseases affecting the affluent countries will spread to the so-called underdeveloped societies.[11]

22

Out of all these fantastic experiments come awareness that as human life becomes more and more dependent on science and technology, more crammed into cities, it becomes more vulnerable to the slightest miscarriage of unforeseen consequences of new innovations. The orthodox methods of science, therefore, must be supplemented by others which come closer to the human experience of reality. One hard aspect of reality is stressed by the scientists themselves: the existence of free will, of creativity, of surprise in human affairs. Men do not simply react, they respond. It is this existence of free will — something presently, and perhaps forever, outside the limits of scientific inquiry — that gives man his uniqueness and marks him so sharply from the rest of the animal kindom. It is free will that brings man to the threshold of choice: to conscious and deliberate awareness of long-term consequences — to an ability to refuse short-term gains for larger and longer implications. It is man alone who has the possibility to see the primacy of secondary consequences. How man uses this free will turns us into a final avenue of inquiry — who is man?

Spiritual Meaning: Who is Man?

Man's perception of himself has been profoundly influenced by scientists whose findings, when unqualifiedly accepted by laymen, suggest that man is an animal. It has been influenced by philosophers whose findings, when unqualifiedly accepted by laymen, suggest that man, being the measure of all things, is himself a god. It has been profoundly influenced by the Bible which tells us that as a creature of God man seeks hungrily for communion with his Maker. Their quest now turns from inquiry into the human being into asking what it means to be human. Rabbi Abraham Heschel will address himself directly to this problem. If we learn more of man and more of society can life itself be programmed? Prepackaged? Preplanned to a point where man ceases to be a problem to himself, and therefore, to his fellowmen and to society? Veils of inadequate understanding will be removed by scholars but will the essential mystery of man remain?

So the operational turning point comes in Professor Boulding's paper as men seek ways to create an integrative society. Love, loyalty, legitimacy — these are the ingredients, says Boulding, which best unify men into a common sense of brotherhood. Yet how shall the hungered-for integration be achieved? By listening to Miguel de Unamuno who urges you to

> Give yourself to others: but in order
> to give yourself to them, first dominate
> your neighbor . . . ; in order to dominate
> your neighbor you must know him and love
> him. . . . My endeavor is to impose myself on
> another: to be and to live in him, to make
> him mine — which is the same as making
> myself his — is that which gives meaning to
> religious collectivity, to human solidarity.[12]

Is life only love, and love itself pity? Or is the answer found in Ayn Rand's novel *Atlas Shrugged* when hero John Gault says: "By my life and my love of it I will never live for the sake of another man, nor ask another man to live for me."[13] Or will integration come when Richard Goodwin analyzes and insists so eloquently on reversing the trend toward centralized government and returning local powers to local people?

The American is seeking to resurrect one of the persisting values of American life. It was a value stated by Yale historian, Ralph Gabriel at the beginning of his interesting volume on American history. The values of America, said Gabriel, were belief in God, belief in the special role of this country and *belief in individualism*. Now we are told that individualism has been thwarted, that God is dead, and that this country had better forget its messianic complex. What shall we cede? What shall we fight to retain? These are the answers desperately sought because in a time of fantastic change certain stabilizers are desperately required.

Conclusion

How fast we are changing can be gleaned by noting the terminal points of the first and second Arden House Conference respectively. Five years ago when the first session was convened there was no COMSAT, no deep wounds in the American conscience from Viet-

24

nam, no Department of Housing and Urban Development, no Department of Transportation, no talk explicitly of a Great Society, no LSD, no Berkeleys, no Beatles. The initials, LBJ, seemed destined for entombment in that vast sepulcher of neglect that Americans have so ingeniously carved for Vice Presidents — and, indeed, for their "number two" men generally. The style, the rhetoric, the dreams were incarnated in JFK. Kennedy's tragic death three years ago teaches a profound lesson. The passing of the President left the nation numb and forelorn — almost in a state of stupor. Yet the recovery was so remarkably quick that we soon forgot the chillness that gripped the heart of man. And in that forgetting we may have forgotten something more important than even the man himself. It is the lesson that men sacrifice to sustain only that which commands their allegiances. And this command depends, in turn, on how the social system conveys to each individual a sense of his own dignity and worth as a man.

Leaders from the life insurance business will ponder this relationship seriously. Instant wisdom will not be theirs but deep resolution to the work of value restoration must be clearly evident. It is not simply the questions asked, but the style of the asking and the style of implementing the answers that are important to man. These styles remind us that man may behave arrogantly, ignorantly or humbly. He has shown arrogance toward colonial peoples under mercantilism, toward blue-collar workers under industrial capitalism, toward Negroes under racialism. He has, in addition, behaved ignorantly by hiding his head, ostrich-like, in the sands — unaware of the vast powers to alter wrong. Isolationism is a case in point. Americans have also behaved humbly as in the case of the Marshall Plan toward Europe and treaty-making with a prostrate Japan.

The insurance leadership of America may have, like the nation itself, exhibited these three manifestations of behavior. Will the lessons to be carried away from this Arden House Conference prove reassuring to all who have responsibility and concern for this important industry? Insurance seeks to make individuals both responsible for their own fates and secure in their own financial destinies. Insurance leaders are showing clearly another important facet: that busy men, powerful men, affluent men are also concerned men. They are concerned with the problems of their society, the problems of their less fortunate fellowmen, the problems of their own integrity as moral beings!

[1] Daniel J. Elazar, "Are We a Nation of Cities?" *The Public Interest* (Summer, 1966), pp. 40-58.

[2] *Ibid.*, p. 53.

[3] Heckscher, *infra.*, pp. 74-86.

[4] Harry Woolf, ed., *Science as a Cultural Force* (Baltimore: The Johns Hopkins Press, 1964), p. 39.

[5] Jacques Barzun, "Science as a Social Institution": *Proceedings of the Academy of Political Science,* XXVIII (April 1, 1966), pp.10-11. Referred to hereafter as *Proceedings.*

[6] Caryl P. Haskins: Science in the Service of Mankind: *Proceedings,* pp. 76-90.

[7] René Dubos, "Science and Man's Future" *The Graduate Journal of Rockefeller University,* VIII (Winter, 1965), pp. 45-67.

[8] Lord Brain, "Knowing Our Minds Better," *The New Scientist* (March 26, 1964), pp. 806-807.

[9] *Ibid.*, pp. 807-8. Shortly after this report was prepared Professor John R. Platt addressed himself imaginatively to some of these same problems in an article entitled "Diversity," *Science.* CCLIV (Dec. 2, 1966), pp. 1132-1139.

[10] Kenneth Boulding, *The Meaning of the Twentieth Century* (New York: Harper and Row, 1964), p. 135.

[11] *Man and His Environment* (Washington: Pan-American Health Organization, 1966). Scientific Paper 131, pp. 7-10.

[12] Miguel de Unamuno, *The Tragic Sense of Life* (New York, Dover Publications, 1954), p. 9.

[13] Ayn Rand, *Atlas Shrugged* (New York: The New American Library — Signet, 1957), p. 136.

CHAPTER 2

Science and the Human Person

René J. Dubos, Ph.D.

Professor, The Rockefeller University

Japanese teenagers of the 1960's are in general very much taller than their parents, and their social behavior differs sharply from that of teenagers in preceding generations. They have inherited the genetic constitution of their progenitors and are still obviously Japanese, but the post-war conditions of life in Japan have profoundly altered the manifestations of their heredity. As is well known, similar phenomena have been observed in other parts of the world for almost a century. In all countries that have become Westernized, young people are growing taller and achieving sexual maturity earlier, not because of changes in their genetic constitution, but probably because they are better protected against infection and malnutrition during their formative years.

The preceding paragraph might be construed as implying that nurture (environment) is more important than nature (genetic endowment) in determining human characteristics. In reality, the ancient nature vs. nurture controversy dealt with a pseudo-problem arising from incomplete knowledge of the mechanisms of physical and mental development. Contrary to popular belief, genes do not predetermine the traits of a person; they merely govern the responses of that person to the forces of the total environment. Bodily shape, physiological functions, and mental attributes are unquestionably under the control of the instructions inscribed in the genetic code characteristic of each person. But all the expressions of the genes are influenced by diet, microbial parasites, social milieu and countless other environmental factors.

Detailed observations of living plants, animals and men have confirmed the commonsense view that, while all the potentialities of an organism are determined by heredity, the total environment regulates the manner and extent to which these potentialities are expressed during life. Recent laboratory findings point indeed to a cellular mechanism through which environmental forces can modify the expressions of the genetic endowment. It has been found that in any living organism only a small percentage of the genes are in an active state at any given time. There is much evidence that various environmental stimuli can set in motion physiological processes capable of acting as repressors or activators of genes. Man is as much an expression of the environment as of his genetic endowment because the actualization of his hereditary potentialities is influenced by environmental forces.

The Experiential and Social Past

All human beings have fundamentally the same anatomical structure, function through the same chemical activities, exhibit the same physiological manifestations and are driven by the same biological urges; yet no two human beings are alike. Clearly, knowledge of the attributes shared by all of mankind is not sufficient to account for the manner in which a particular person develops his own physical and mental peculiarities, behaves as he does, in brief becomes different from all other human beings.

Except for the special case of identical offspring in multiple births, individual persons differ in their genetic makeup. But this constitutes only one determinant of individuality. As important is the fact that the characteristics of individual human beings are constantly being molded and altered by environmental factors which endlessly vary with time, differ from one place to the other and are never the same for two different persons. Even identical twins become different if raised in dissimilar environments.

Recent studies have given substance to the ancient awareness that many characteristics of the adult human being result from the effects of "early influences," namely those environmental factors that impinge on the person during early life while he is still developing. Such formative effects can take place even in the

28

womb. For example, even though the Dionne quintuplets were genetically identical, and had been treated as alike as possible after birth, they could be recognized as individuals from the very beginning of their life, probably because the position of each one of the sisters during intrauterine life had differently affected her development. Likewise early postnatal influences affect profoundly almost every characteristic — from nutritional needs and morphological appearance to learning ability and emotional attitudes. The effects of early influences, both prenatal and postnatal, become so deeply rooted in the biological structure of the person involved that they usually persist throughout the whole life span.

Comparative anatomical studies of the various organs at different times after conception and after birth have done much to account for the profound, lasting, and often peculiar effects exerted by environmental factors on the developing organism. Different tissues and different areas of the body grow at different rates throughout the formative period, either prenatal or postnatal. This fact accounts not only for the changes that occur in body shape as development proceeds, but also for the differences in response made by the various organs to environmental forces in relation to their age. The development of the brain is naturally of special interest in this regard because it has such direct relevance to the problems of learning and behavior.

Neural development is profoundly affected for example by the nutritional state, infectious processes and other environmental factors which influence health and disease. Thus, some of the largest problems of human growth and behavior revolve around the effects that the physiological conditions of upbringing, and the social environment, including all early influences and educational experiences, exert at different periods of life on the development of the body and the brain.

The environmental influences that are ubiquitous in a given geographical area or social group naturally tend to bring out many characteristics common to all members of the group. For this reason there is much truth in Emerson's statement that "We resemble our contemporaries even more than our progenitors." But environmental influences also affect each person in an individual manner, even when the ways of life appear uniform in a standardized environment. Genetic uniqueness makes for differ-

29

ences in response and consequently for singularities in mental and physical development. Each one of us lives, as it were, in a private world of his own.

Generally speaking, environmental influences shape personality through two different types of mechanisms. On the one hand, they determine certain patterns of response that affect all manifestations of behavior. Physiologists, psychologists, psychiatrists and writers have described each in his own way a seemingly endless variety of acquired responses ranging from the salivation of dogs at the sound of a bell, to the pathological effects of the Freudian complexes, or the remembrance of things past evoked by a madeleine dipped into a cup of tea. On the other hand, environmental influences contribute to the shaping of personality by interfering with the acquisition of new experiences. In order to be able to continue developing mentally, a person should ideally remain receptive to new stimuli, new events, and new situations. In fact, however, the ability to apprehend the external world with freshness of perception commonly decreases as the mind and the senses become conditioned by repeated experiences.

Human beings thus perceive the world, and respond to it, not through the whole spectrum of their genetic potentialities, but only through the areas of this spectrum that have not been blocked by inhibitory mechanisms and that have been made functional by environmental influences, especially the early ones. The word "potentiality" is meant here to denote the whole range of the organism's genetic endowment, whether the characteristics involved are physical or mental in nature. In other words, life experiences determine what parts of this endowment become expressed in the form of functional attributes.

The biological and psychological processes set in motion by the interplay between human beings provide striking examples of the lasting and profound influence that the past exerts on modern man. Because he evolved as a social animal, man cannot develop well physically and mentally, or even long remain normal, unless he maintains close associations with other human beings. On the other hand, crowding and excess of social contacts may overstimulate certain of his hormonal activities and thereby have undesirable consequences. There are definite thresholds with regard to the nature and intensity of the social stimuli that can safely impinge on the human organism, but these thresholds differ according to the history of the person concerned and of his group. Qualitatively and quantitatively, man's responses to the social environment are conditioned not only by his genetic endowment and his early experiences, but also by the traditional conventions and values of the groups within which he developed and in which he functions. Man's nature is inevitably conditioned by his social past. Usually man passively accepts the traditions of his group as embodying the truth; but even when he rebels against them, the new traditions he tries to create always incorporate many of the ancient ways and thus continue to make him dependent on his social past.

Man Makes Himself

Biologically, man has not changed much since late paleolithic times. The implements he made during the Stone Age still fit our hands; the ancient drives that first shaped his tribal activities are still operative in us; the paintings and sculptures of cave art, the artifacts symbolizing prehistoric beliefs still affect us emotionally and esthetically. However, while *Homo sapiens* has remained essentially the same from the genetic point of view, the manifestations of his life, and the structure of his societies are endlessly changing. The very concept of progress implies that the events of human social life never repeat themselves identically. The permanency of man's nature resides in the chemical structure of the genetic code controlling the biological materials out of which his body and brain are made; the change in man's life comes from the creative responses that he and his societies make to the challenges of the total environment. To live is to respond, and thereby to activate the mechanisms responsible for creative adaptation.

Biological sciences have gone far toward defining the chemical structures and physiological processes of the human body; they are even beginning to apprehend the mechanisms of mental processes. But they cannot explain how each person becomes what he is, and so to speak makes himself through a continuous series of personal decisions.

As used here, the phrase "personal decisions" implies of course that man possesses free will. Unfortunately, the concept of free will is at present, and perhaps forever, outside the limits of scientific inquiry. It must be used nevertheless because free will represents such an obvious and essential part of human experience. Whatever their mechanism, the interventions of free will limit the ability of biological knowledge to account completely for the living man whom the humanist tries to apprehend and the artist to express.

A few remarks concerning the plastic arts will illustrate the manner in which man's ability to choose and decide limits of the relevance of biological knowledge to the understanding of man's nature. The paintings, statues, engravings and other artifacts found in paleolithic sites leave no doubt that the faculty for artistic expression is very ancient; indeed, it does not seem to have significantly improved over the past 20,000 years with regard either to acuity of perception or to skill in representation. There is every reason to believe that the ability to perceive and to represent corresponds to deeply-seated physiological attributes of man's nature.

The esthetic faculty as it exists in man is probably based on biological attributes analogous to those which make animals perform movements or build nests having an intrinsic harmony. Whether the satisfaction derived from the way our senses or organs react to certain patterns and other stimuli has a purely genetic basis, or is the product of conditioning influences experienced in early life, is irrelevant here. The point of importance is that esthetic consciousness depends on faculties that are biological in essence and have not changed significantly since the Stone Age.

However the ability to perceive and to represent is not sufficient by itself to create human works of art; artistic creation involves other factors that fall outside the realm of the natural sciences. While human beings respond to their environment through their biological attributes, they do not react passively as if they were just mechanical intermediaries in stimulus-response couplets. The artist's response is not mechanical, nor motivated by the desire to cope practically with the environment; it constitutes rather an expressive behavior in which the artist uses the environment for the purpose of self-actualization, and at times to transcend himself.

The act of artistic creation thus provides a convenient example to illustrate the role of human choices in deciding on a certain course of action among the possibilities that are available for dealing with external nature through the needs, drives and urges inherent in man's nature. All aspects of human life present opportunities for active intervention on the part of man — the one creature who can consciously choose, eliminate, assemble, decide and thereby move toward some selected goal.

In a surprising but very real way, man becomes what he does. Through the complex feedbacks that govern all of life, man's biological endowment creates his culture and is in turn modified by his culture. Man is what he is today because he has been doing cultural and intellectual things for the past few millenia. The kind of creature he will become will be determined by the kind of activities he elects to emphasize in his life.

The powers of action generated by scientific advances are so great that the classical discussions on the ideals of the good life now take on very practical meaning. In meeting the dangers and exploiting the opportunities of the modern world, human beings will be guided not only by scientific knowledge and technology, but also by the beliefs they hold and the goals they select. The future of mankind rests on man's ability to take decisions based on ethical and esthetic criteria.

Mankind — that is to say, we — shall drift aimlessly toward a state incompatible with the maintenance of the values from which we derive our uniqueness among living forms, unless we formulate goals worthy of the human condition, and are willing to take a stand at the critical time. In the words of Paul Tillich, "Man becomes truly human only at the moment of decision." This kind of freedom is the final and finest criterion of humanness.

Divine Madness

Even the most rational man retains from his animal and paleolithic past a number of physiological and psychological attributes over which he has little control. Ancient civilizations were aware of the effects of these hidden forces on human behavior and commonly symbolized them by a ferocious bull struggling against reason. More importantly, they regarded irrational urges as a creative force.

Our greatest blessings, says Socrates in *Phaedrus,* come to us by way of madness. Socrates did not mean, of course, that it is better to be mad than sane, sick than sound. Rather, he pleaded for the need to escape from the limitations and conventionalities of rational life and to function independently of social norms. It is a remarkable fact that Plato, the spokesman of rationalism, of submission to the social order, should have advocated a type of behavior which he related to "madness" because he knew it to be dependent on faculties which are more or less uncontrolled and outside the realm of reason. These include, according to Plato, all the primeval forces symbolized in Greek mythology by Bacchus, Aphrodite, Eros, and the Muses; also those mysterious forces symbolized by Apollo which endow man to transcend himself as by a sort of prophetic gift.

In civilized communities today, Socrates' divine madness plays a large role in the mental operations through which man becomes creative and thus gives birth to the future or at least prepares the ground for its emergence. Experience reveals that the creator is by necessity somewhat dissatisfied, often misadapted, even a transgressor, and must transcend the conventions of his group and probably of his public self.

Most ancient societies empirically or consciously devised complex practices designed to supplement the submission to the group (adaptation) with an expression of the subconscious, so-called irrational components of human personality. The Greeks had systematized these practices in the Dionysiac ceremonies with the use of wine and of the religious dance, aimed at providing some relief from social discipline and perhaps also some enlargement of life under the guise of collective experience. For them Dionysus was Lusios, "the Liberator." The aim of his cult was *ecstasis,* which could mean anything from "taking you out of yourself" to a profound alteration of personality.

Ecstasis is certainly more than liberation. It corresponds to an attitude as essential for creation as for true happiness. Life in the "Land of the Lotus eaters," may be comfortable and free of care, but man is not satisfied with this kind of gratification. He remains healthy and creative only if his environment gives him the chance to express the full range of his potentialities, even some of those that appear irrational.

Environment for Man

Each person has a wide range of latent innate potentialities. Whether physical or mental, these potentialities can become actualized only to the extent that circumstances are favorable to their existential expression. Society thus plays a large role in the unfolding and development of the human personality.

The conditioning of the physical and mental personality by the environment has of course long been recognized. Winston Churchill was aware of its importance for human life when he urged that the House of Commons, damaged during the War, be rebuilt as exactly as possible in its original form, instead of being replaced by a modern and more efficient building. He feared that changing the physical appearance and organization of the House might alter the character of Parliamentary debates and therefore of English democracy. In his words, "We shape our buildings, and then they shape us."

One can take it for granted that the latent potentialities of human beings have a better chance to become actualized when the social environment is sufficiently diversified to provide a variety of stimulating experience, especially for the young. As more persons are given the opportunity to express the individual peculiarities of their biological endowment under diversified conditions, society becomes richer in experiences and civilizations continue to unfold. In contrast, if the surroundings and ways of life are highly stereotyped, the only components of man's nature that flourish are those adapted to the narrow range of prevailing conditions.

Irrespective of genetic endowment, a child who grows up in a city slum will differ as an adult from one who has spent most of his early life within the four walls of a mechanized high rise apartment, or from one who has participated in the chores of a family farm. Unfortunately, the awareness that surroundings exert a profound effect on human life is based largely on untutored observations and has not yet been converted into scientific knowledge.

Environmental factors condition all aspects of human life but nobody really knows which precise factors are influential or how they work. The problem however is not hopeless. Experiments have revealed that in animals also, early influences condition growth, longevity, behavior, resistance to stress and learning ability. It can

35

be taken for granted, therefore, that the effects exerted on human life by early influences can be studied through the use of experimental models much as is being done for other types of biological problems. The knowledge thus acquired will certainly help in the rational management of society.

One lesson to be derived from the story of evolution is that man has been so successful because he is the least specialized creature on earth and the most adaptable. He can hunt or farm, be a meat eater or a vegetarian, live in the mountains or by the seashore, be a loner or engage in team work, function in a free democracy or under aristocratic leadership.

History shows furthermore that societies that were once efficient because they were highly specialized, rapidly collapsed when conditions changed. A highly specialized society is rarely adaptable. Adaptability is essential for social as well as for biological success. Therein lies the danger of the standardization and regimentation so prevalent in modern life. Uniformity of environment is as much of a curse as absolute conformity in behavior.

To sum up: it is certain that the characteristics of individual persons, and of societies, are profoundly affected by feedback reactions between man's nature and environmental forces. Man has much freedom in selecting and creating his environment, as well as his ways of life, and he determines by such decisions what he and his descendants will become. In this light man can truly "make himself," consciously and willfully. He has the privilege of responsible choice for his destiny — probably the noblest attribute of the human condition.

CHAPTER 3

The Changing Brain in a Changing Society

José M. R. Delgado, M.D.

**Department of Physiology and Psychiatry
Yale University School of Medicine**

In our rapidly changing society there is an increasing need to understand the evolutionary trends of civilization, to foresee the advances of technology and to plan our adaptation to new environments which will have physical and social characteristics without parallel in the past history of man. The art of forecasting, once the special domain of the social sciences, now permeates all scholarly circles. For example, the American Academy of Arts and Sciences is sponsoring a study on predictions for the year 2,000, and different institutions, including Columbia University, which organized the present Arden House Conference, are also trying to analyze the forces that will play basic roles in structuring our future civilization.

If we were asked to single out the most important developments responsible for changes in the present world and for the future of man, we could mention mass communication, computers and atomic energy among the spectacular accomplishments of physics. There are also other more subtle developments which may have as much, if not more, influence on the future evolution of society, and both their value and their implications need special emphasis.

The research described in this article was supported by grants from the United States Public Health Service and the Office of Naval Research, and was performed with the collaboration of Mrs. Caroline S. Delgado.

Freedom of Choice

In contrast with limitations experienced by members of primitive societies, we have almost endless possibilities to pursue our interests and activities as we see fit. Modern life is not bound by physical restrictions of geography; our voices can be transmitted with the speed of light to any person around the world; with television we can see events in any country as they actually happen; and we can travel at supersonic speed to distant lands. We are not limited in food intake by our hunting skills or by seasonal variations affecting crops. Instead, we have access to a variety of markets and supermarkets providing the culinary products of many nations and climates. In the acquisition of knowledge we are no longer dependent on verbal contact, but have access to many centers of learning equipped with an increasing variety of teaching aides. We are able to choose from a wide variety of material goods, entertainment, friends, careers, ideologies and religions. Even parenthood may be planned, conception timed and birth controlled by proper use of modern medical knowledge.

Today our activities are less determined by adaptation to nature than by the creativity and foresight of the human mind which recently has added another dimension to its spectrum of choices: the possibility of investigating its own physical and chemical substratum, within brain physiology. Limitation and control of our behavior are imposed mainly by the by-products of civilization, education, legislation, social pressure and economic conditions, rather than by environmental determination as was formerly the case. In spite of the increase in possible courses of action, the freedom an individual enjoys is relatively small because of the confinement and regimentation of a complex and increasingly mechanized society. Liberation from ecology is paralleled by a mechanized servitude which absorbs large amounts of manpower for the invention, construction and maintenance of machines.

Independent behavior is related to the availability of different types of response but knowledge of the determining factors and possible behavioral choices are important. Awareness of the intervening elements and mechanisms is essential to diminish automatism and to increase consciousness, discrimination, individualism and independence in the personal conduct.

Awareness

The most distinctive qualities which separate man from other species are awareness of his own existence and the capacity to control and change what would be his natural fate. Awareness is a rather expensive luxury in time and effort and we must realize that most of our daily tasks are only a complex series of automatisms. Walking, for example, requires a tedious process of learning. Babies spend many hours in trial-and-error testing of their motor responses but when the ideokinetic formulas have been established no attention is necessary to the onset, strength, speed, timing and sequences of muscular performance. These processes are automatic and to a great extent characteristic for each individual. We can, however, refocus our attention on any motor aspect to re-educate and modify the motor formulas, improving, for example, the gracefulness of walking, or mimicking the gait of sailors, tramps and cowboys, as actors must do to represent them on stage.

Stopping our car at a red light does not require judgment or decision because we are highly trained and conditioned to this performance. But if we pause to analyze our own behavior, we may be aware of the motor activity necessary to press the car brakes and of the reasons for stopping and for obeying traffic rules, which only then may be questioned or even ignored. Choice is not involved in an automatic response. If we reappraise the reasons and circumstances surrounding our actions, new avenues of response may be opened. This possibility applies to emotional reactions and social behavior as well as to motor activity.

Awareness is increased by knowledge of the mechanisms of the considered phenomena. For example, a mechanic may hear different sounds when a car motor is running and may perceive messages which are not detected by the ordinary driver. Familiarity with the structure and function of a motor permits us to foresee, prevent and correct possible malfunction.

To a considerable extent our personal behavior is a response to sensory inputs and shows a high degree of automatism. If we knew the genetic factors, cultural elements and intracerebral mechanisms involved in the various kinds of behavioral performance, we could understand the reasons for acting as we do. If we were aware of the

39

intervening factors we could accept or reject many of them and minimize their effects upon us. The result would be a decrease in automatism and an increase in the intelligent quality of our responses to the environment.

Responsibility

Savage man could not consider whether he was going to spend the afternoon at the movies, reading a book or watching television. He was continuously occupied with the struggle for survival. Our wide choice of how to spend our time requires of us a continuous mental effort to understand and evaluate different possibilities, to think about the implications of each one, to modify or repress emotional reactions to each and make a final decision. In many cases these processes are performed at the subconscious level and responses flow effortlessly, but at other times there is awareness of alternative conflicting ideas and then the decision may be difficult and tiresome. The deliberate selection of one path among many demands a greater responsibility from the individual because his activities are no longer determined either by automatic mechanisms, external factors beyond his control or blind forces of nature. Rational and intelligent judgment is based on the individual's personal qualities and ability to accept or reject a variety of behavioral solutions. Individual choice represents responsibility for the direction of personal destiny. Greater awareness and freedom result in larger responsibility. In a small social group, as in a tribe, the consequences of the leader's choice are rather limited. But in highly organized societies, decisions of governmental elites will affect a large number of people. The political decisions of contemporary powerful nations on such issues as foreign aid, cultural exchange and especially peace and war will affect conditions in most of the world. Decisions like these always represent the activity of intracerebral mechanisms of which little is known.

Accumulation of Power

Industrial and technological developments have created an unparalleled amount of resources with immense constructive and destructive potential. The natural obstacles of rivers, seas and mountains have already been conquered and are no longer insurmountable barriers to the activities of man. At the same time, we have accumulated megatons of energy capable of annihilating the entire world population.

Instruments have been invented to increase a millionfold the sensitivity of our senses, the power of our muscles and our ability to process information. In addition to augmenting our material power, we have greatly improved our capacity to organize and use available resources. Plans for the development of cities, industries, research, education and the economy in general are carefully laid down by experts, and these plans are essential for the organization and evolution of our society. These facts again bring up the question of responsibility in the choice of objectives to be reached. Because of the magnitude of our material and intellectual powers and the fact that they are controlled by small directive groups, decisions may have such transcendency that the very existence of man may depend on our foresight and intelligence in solving possible conflicts.

To some extent, the relations between man and nature were reversed when man's initial ecological dependence was replaced by his domination of natural forces. Rivers were no longer obstacles to communication, but became elements to transport merchandise and people and to provide hydroelectric energy. The earth has ceased to be a predominantly hostile place of inhospitable mountains and deserts, wild forests and predatory animals. It is being transformed into a submissive land of houses, gardens, crops and cattle. Human power has changed the aspect of nature by drilling tunnels through mountains, destroying and planting forests, cultivating fields, constructing bridges, highways and cities. The evolution of many animal species has been decisively altered through breeding techniques so that while most predatory beasts have disappeared from civilized countries, other species useful to man, such as the chicken, sheep and cow, have increased in number and have been modified in quality as a result of human efforts.

Major nations are constantly faced with the choice of how to use their power. Conscious efforts are being exerted to make intelligent decisions in establishing national goals such as overcoming poverty, landing men on the moon or meeting timetables for industrial, agricultural and scientific development. Education and public health also have their place among national goals, but the emphasis remains on technology and the domination of nature, not on the improvement of psychological qualities of man. As our resources are not unlimited, a major effort in one field, such as armaments or outer space, will restrict the development of other less favored areas. The application of human energy in controlling the forces of nature is continually increasing. Perhaps it is time to ask whether the present orientation of our civilization is desirable and sound, or whether we should re-examine the universal goals of mankind in the hope of finding better solutions of unsolved problems.

Imbalance Between Material and Mental Evolution

Originally, philosophy and science were unified in their purpose, which was, in the words of Plato, "the vision of truth." They were also unified in their methodological exploration of reality which consisted of observation and rational interpretation of what was observed. This congenial relation persisted for many centuries until ideological and technological revolutions introduced new methodologies and the need for greater specialization. Unable to resolve their developing differences in outlook and method, philosophy and science separated from one another, tearing apart what had been their common subject of inquiry. Philosophers and theologians carried with them the mind and soul; scientists kept matter and the body. This left newcomers like the psychologists to live, for a while, a schizophrenic existence between spirit and substance with neither scientific recognition nor philosophical support.

Mathematics, physics and chemistry became increasingly important fields of study, and the application of experimental methods of biology was so fruitful that scholarly interest was diverted from philosophy to science. Why spend time in semantic fencing and speculation when the important questions could be put directly to the stars, rocks and living organisms?

Telescopes and microscopes explored opposite aspects of the natural world and organic compounds were synthesized. The exploding sciences engaged most of the available intellectual and economic resources, directing them toward industry, biology, electronics, atomic energy, outer space exploration and similar fields of endeavor. In contrast, only a minor fraction was devoted to the inquiry into the nature of mental faculties. This unbalanced situation was determined in part by methodological reasons. The mind was considered a metaphysical entity beyond experimental reach. Despite the obvious importance of understanding the psychological essence of man, it was more practical to invent combustion engines or to investigate the structure of cells than to speculate about emotions and thoughts. While it is true that the disciplines of psychology and psychiatry have greatly expanded in our century, a decade or two ago the brain was still treated as a "black box" which could be reached only through the senses. Psychological investigations analyzed correlations between sensory inputs and behavioral outputs but could not explore the processes lying in between which were hidden in the unknowns of brain physiology. Some authors doubted that study of neurons could throw any light on understanding the properties of the mind. Surprisingly enough, most investigators of the brain also contributed to the imbalance of this situation because they studied heavily anesthetized subjects, thus dealing with sleepy neurons and failing to take into account the mental complexity of the waking brain.

The contrast between the fast pace of technological evolution and our limited advances in the understanding and control of human behavior is creating a growing danger. We are facing a situation in which vast amounts of accumulated destructive power are at the disposal of brains which have not yet learned to be wise enough to solve economic conflicts and ideological antagonisms intelligently. The "balance of terror" existing in the present world reflects the imbalance between the awesome technology and underdeveloped wisdom of man. There is urgency in finding methods for re-education and for the control of social antagonisms and undesirable emotional manifestations. While these processes are obviously related to environmental circumstances, they also depend on the activity of intracerebral mechanisms which are unknown and ignored. When primitive man faced natural catastrophes such as floods or pestilence, he was helpless and reacted with resignation or despair, or he appealed to supernatural powers. In contrast, modern man, being more perceptive, may decide to study his circumstances and apply his power and intelligence to the immediate problem. By constructing dikes or vaccinating the populace, he may prevent or modify the forces of natural causality. It is reasonable to assume that just as a better knowledge of natural mechanisms allows us to use and control natural forces, a better understanding of the central nervous system should allow us to educate and direct more intelligently the activity of the mind. The necessary information may be provided by recently developed methodology for the direct exploration of the conscious, behaving brain, which represents a powerful means to investigate and influence behavioral and mental activities.

Study Of Brain Mechanisms In Behaving Subjects

In animals and in man the depth of the brain is like an ocean through which we can navigate without visibility by relying on instrumental guidance. Anatomists have constructed suitable cerebral maps, oriented according to stereotaxic coordinates, which permit the blind placement of electrodes within any desired structure. Very fine wires, guided mechanically by micromanipulators, are introduced through a small opening made in the skull. The terminal contacts are exteriorized outside the skin and used for electrical stimulation or recording. The surgical operation is performed under anesthesia, and as the electrodes remain implanted for days or even for life, studies may be carried out in completely awake subjects who are engaged in spontaneous normal activities.

The idea of leaving wires inside the living brain could seem uncomfortable and dangerous, but actually experience has shown that this procedure is safe and painless. Patients have been wired for months without expressing any concern or discomfort, enjoying a normal life and returning to the hospital only for periodic stimulations. There are several medical indications which require implantation of electrodes inside the human brain. In some cases of drug-resistant epilepsy it is necessary to explore the depth of subcortical regions in order to detect areas with abnormal discharges and to orient subsequent surgical treatment. Patients with intractable pain, anxiety neurosis, involuntary movements and other illnesses have benefited from the cerebral explorations conducted without the confinement and stress of the operating room.

In reality, the use of electrodes represents a more conservative approach than the destruction of portions of the brain for the treatment of neural disabilities. In some cases long term stimulations may substitute for the placement of lesions, thereby obviating the destruction of cerebral tissue.

In addition to its therapeutic use, implantation of electrodes represents an important tool for the investigation of neurophysiological processes in animals such as cats, monkeys and chimpanzees. Much valuable data is rapidly accumulating, as shown in the reviews by Sheer[1], Ramey and O'Doherty[2] and Delgado.[3]

The presence of leads connecting experimental subject and instrumentation represented a serious obstacle for free behavioral expression and for long term stimulation. This problem has been solved with the use of remote controlled miniaturized apparatus carried by the subject. Very recently we have developed special circuits under the name of "Stimoceivers" which permit both transmission and reception of electrical messages to and from the brain by means of a frequency modulated radio link. The next step which is now being tested in our laboratory will be the subcutaneous implantation of miniaturized integrated circuits enclosed in biologically inert silicon. This future instrument will be totally passive. Its energy will be transferred through the skin by radio induction which will make it possible to stimulate and record intracerebral activity in the absence of exterior leads. With this system animals or humans could be instrumented for life for the monitoring of electrical activity and for delivery of intermittent or continuous stimulations by means of timing mechanisms. Important therapeutic applications may be expected from this methodology.

In animals, electric stimulation of motor structures of the brain result in well organized movements which are usually indistinguishable from voluntary activity. Some of these effects are simple responses such as flexing a leg, closing an eye or opening the mouth. In other cases, depending on the structure stimulated, the motor performance includes a determined sequence of acts of varied complexity. Excitation of the red nucleus in monkeys, for example, has produced a change in facial expression followed by turning of the head, standing on two feet, circling, walking on two feet, climbing, low toned vocalization, threatening and approaching other animals. This complex and ordered sequence was repeated as many times as the red nucleus was stimulated. Evoked effects are reliable if the situation is maintained constant but will adapt to changes in the experimental setup. For example, an external threat of waving the catching net in front of the monkey induced a precipitous escape, inhibiting most of the motor effects evoked by cerebral stimulation, unless the applied electrical intensity was rather strong. In general, we have observed a play of forces between spontaneous and artificial responses with an algebraic summation of the resultant effect. The conclusion reached after a considerable amount of experimentation was that behavior is organized as motor fragments which have anatomical and functional representation within the brain. These fragments may be combined in different ways like the notes of a melody, resulting in a succession of motor acts which constitute specific behavioral categories, such as walking or eating. These formulas of motor activity may be activated in a similar way by the spontaneous "will" of the subject, or by artificial electrical stimulation of determined areas of the brain, providing an excellent opportunity for analysis of the cerebral mechanisms of behavioral performance.

Even more interesting have been the results obtained by electrical stimulation of areas of the brain which play a role in emotional responses. In these cases the evoked effect is not a stereotyped movement, but a change in general reactivity toward environmental inputs. For example, in restrained monkeys, stimulation of the tegmentum, central gray, midline thalamus and several other structures evoked a typical offensive reaction with showing of teeth, low toned vocalization, flattening of the ears, staring, restlessness and general threatening attitude. When the same areas were stimulated by radio while the monkey was completely free forming part of a colony, the results depended on the hierarchical status and on the social situation. When radio stimulation was applied to the boss, his aggression was preferentially directed against a particular monkey, usually an unfriendly male, and never against the female who had been his favorite companion and playmate. It should be emphasized that the increased aggressiveness of the boss depended on the electrical stimulation of the brain. The motor details of aggressive performance and the direction of the hostility were determined by the previous experience of the animal and by the location and reactions of his enemies. This fact proved that the emotional state of anger could be differentiated experimentally from the actual performance and suggested that they were related to different cerebral mechanisms which could be influenced independently of each other.

In agreement with these ideas were the results obtained by cerebral stimulation in some of our patients. For example, in A........ F........, who was a boy with temporal lobe epilepsy, electrical excitation of the second temporal convolution elicited an eightfold increase in friendly manifestations and in verbal output quantified by the number of words per minute. The effect was highly specific because it did not appear when other areas of the brain were stimulated. While the increase in communication and in affectiveness depended on the artificially applied electricity, the facial expression, chosen words, phrases used and ideological content of the conversation were in agreement with the education and mental capacity of the patient. His basic personality had not been modified, only his effective tone and expressive aspect.

These results introduce many important questions about cerebrobehavioral correlations. Could friendliness be related with functional activation of determined areas of the brain? May this activation be induced in a similar way by specific psychic messages and by unspecific electrical signals? Can we interpret emotional tone as a cerebral bias which will modulate sensory input from the environment? These and many other questions will require more experimentation and intellectual elaboration, but the results obtained in animals and humans show that we have the necessary tools for investigation of the neuronal basis of emotional and behavioral reactions, and also that we can influence psychic functions by direct stimulation of the brain. These facts indicate that the brain and its functional counterpart, mental activities, are within experimental reach. What is necessary now is a great effort to investigate the basic cerebral mechanisms related to the essence of man and to direct our own intellect towards the understanding and control of our emotional and behavioral activities. Regaining of mental balance over technology should be decisive for a happier and more intelligent future evolution of man.

The Changing Brain

It is well known that we are living in a rapidly changing society which is enjoying and suffering the consequences of a powerful technological revolution, but perhaps the most important application of technology has passed unnoticed. In my opinion the fact that we can investigate and influence the biological mechanisms of behavioral and mental activities by physical and chemical means is more important than the spectacular accomplishments of atomic research or outer space exploration, because we may now deal with the very essence of man. It would, however, be naive to suppose that we will be able to explain the thinking process in terms of biochemical concepts and electrical fields, as it would be misleading to describe a sculpture in only geometric terms. In the study of mental activity we must distinguish the *material carriers* which can be expressed as *physical* static and dynamic properties, from the *symbolic meaning* which is related to the *past experience* of each individual organism and requires knowledge of *individual history*. The same symbol, for example, a black triangle, should activate the sensory receptors of the eye in a similar way in different subjects and even in different species, but depending on previous associations the triangle may represent punishment, reward or may be neutral. The *meaning* is not in the material carrier, but in *temporal associations* among different carriers which probably will determine several other material *subcarriers* to convey the specific meaning. We need to correlate both physical and psychological concepts which will supplement each other. Both are within experimental reach and we can analyze the symbolic (mainly cultural and experimental) and biological mechanisms which intervene in the integration of personal structure and the establishment of social relations.

Intracerebral studies will provide essential data for the correlation of sensory inputs (education) and motor output (behavior). Until recently this problem was investigated only from outside of the organism, and the purpose of education was precisely to obtain socially acceptable patterns of behavior. Investigation of intracerebral physiology will permit us to approach the same problem from the new vantage point of *inside the organism*. The purpose of these studies is not to control behavior by electronics, but to provide vital information about our behavioral and mental mechanisms so that we may educate more intelligent and efficient human beings. If we are aware of the environmental elements which influence us, we will have greater individual freedom to accept or to reject them. If we are aware that emotional states are essentially dependent on the activation of determined cerebral structures, we may diminish automatism and increase rationality in a deliberate effort to have our cerebral structures related to reason and engaged in a play of forces with outer cerebral structures involved in anger or attack. In addition to providing patterning of factual knowledge, ideology, moral principles and behavioral responses, educational systems should also teach the biological mechanisms of mental activity in order to increase our self-awareness and to facilitate greater individual differentiation and elaboration of the patterns given by education.

To adapt to a changing society, a changing brain should be aware of the intervening circumstances to increase free choice and to direct for its own benefit the vast power accumulated by technology. Present aspirations to increase domination of natural power and to achieve greater physical comfort for man must be balanced by greater efforts to investigate the biological bases of human personality. Happiness, after all, is essentially dependent on the interrelation of constellations of neurons which are still unexplored.

[1] Sheer, Daniel E., ed., *Electrical Stimulation of the Brain* (Austin: University of Texas Press, 1961), 641 p.

[2] Ramey, E. R., and O'Doherty, D. S., eds., *Electrical Studies on the Unanesthetized Brain* (New York: Paul B. Hoeber, 1960), 423 p.

[3] Delgado, José M. R., "Free Behavior and Brain Stimulation," *International Review of Neurobiology,* Vol. VI (New York: Academic Press, 1964), pp. 349-449.

Other References

Delgado, José M. R., *Innovation and Experiment in Modern Education* (Washington: American Council on Education, 1965), pp. 121-29.

—— James Arthur Lecture on the Evolution of the Human Brain (New York: American Museum of Natural History, 1965), 54 p.

—— "Emotions," Self-Selection Psychology Textbook (Dubuque, Iowa: W. C. Brown, 1966), 56 p.

—— 1965-66 Jennings Scholar Lectures, pp. 101-12.

CHAPTER 4

MAN — WHO IS HE?

Rabbi Abraham J. Heschel, Ph.D.
Professor of Jewish Ethics and Mysticism
The Jewish Theological Seminary

Should this be another lecture? If I were to repeat what I have said before or done somewhere before in just the same way, I would be a recording; not human, but mechanical. I am supposed to be a human being.

What does it mean to be human?

For example, this speech is being taped. If you play the tape, it is there, but it is detached from you, played by itself, and does not take the listeners into account. A human being is a person who is not detached but is responsive to the situation in which he finds himself.

If I were taped, you would be listening to a meticulously prepared lecture. But there must be another element and that is the element of surprise. A tape is no surprise. Maybe an aspect of being human is the ability to create surprise — to be a surprise.

I would generally describe a person as a being capable of creating events. A baby is born. Look at the infant and try to figure out what will become of this baby. A baby called Johann Sebastian was born to a father, Mr. Bach. That baby created many events. We do not know the pattern of genes of a tiny baby. His future is a surprise.

What is human about a human being? Every human being has a tremendous universe of potential, of surprise and is unpredictable

---

Transcribed from notes taken at the Conference. The substance of this address was taken from a book by A. J. Heschel, *Who Is Man?*, Stanford University Press.

to a considerable degree. Of course, a human being is not all human; therefore much in a human being is predictable — much in a human being is a process rather than an event because a human being is a polarity of being human and being a human being. By human being I mean that man is given to us by nature; being human is the specific realm of humanity — in other words, a combination of process and events.

Process and Events

What is the difference between process and events? A process follows a pattern; an event creates a precedent. This is what is so exciting about a human life and about humanity in general. There are these two dimensions of being a human being and being human. The two are interdependent. I am born a human being, but I have to acquire being human. This, perhaps, is my greatest challenge, a challenge for everybody. This also creates a problem.

Let me stress the importance of this problem. My world consists primarily of students. As I watch, I see that many of them are confused by asking the wrong questions. Philosophy is the search for the right questions. You have won half the battle in research when you have identified the right questions. The tragedy is the preoccupation with wrong questions. Consequently, since the formulation of a question immediately determines the course of your inquiry, wrong formulation misdirects research. We often ask wrong questions about man. We are concerned with marginal, peripheral, often specious issues and not with the central issues.

Let me give you an example of what I mean by asking the right question. A book was published recently and advertised in the *New York Times* about man. I would like to give you some questions answered in it which I am not going to ask. For example, you will find answers in the book to the questions: "Why blondism prevails in northern Europe." "How nose shapes are influenced by climate." Are these the most important questions about man?

The Problem of Man

Now I would like to take one more step. Questions are not enough. There are questions and there are problems. What I would like to deal with is the problem of man. What is the difference between a question and a problem? A question comes out of curiosity — out of not knowing; a problem comes about as a result of knowing too much. My first recommendation is to realize that man is a problem. Our educational system, in particular, and perhaps even other fields may suffer from an oversimplification of man — an oversimplification of human nature. We approach man as too simple a being. I would say man in his very essence is a problem and he remains a problem. There are two ways to deal with a problem: one is to solve it and one is to dissolve it. Some people dissolve it by denying the problem. Then you kill the problem instead of curing it. We have suffered from this a great deal; and we suffer from this on many levels of existence.

We must keep alive, even on the highest level of sophistication, the naive, burning emergency of the human situation. Let me say then again that the very concern with the problem of man indicates that man is a problem. A horse properly cared for is happy. Give a human being everything and he still has problems. If we ever attain a utopia when science, industry and technology have solved all human problems, what a dull species man would be! Everyone of us has at least a vague notion that there is something more to human beings than just being. What is it? There is something at stake in each of us. No one knows the final answer. But it is precisely this awareness that makes us human, and more than mere things like this desk and the floor on which I am standing.

All thinking follows essentially two patterns. One pattern is to try to discover what various phenomena have in common. As I look around in this hall, I know there are certain aspects common to all of us. We are human beings; we are involved in vocations; we all breathe; we all belong to the species *Homo sapiens;* we are all Americans. If I walk in the forest and come upon a flower which I do not quite recognize, my first goal is to classify it. And once I establish its species, I say to myself that I have a great knowledge about that particular flower.

But now what do I do if I am about to write a biography of Napoleon? I will read you an imaginary biography of Napoleon. When Napoleon was born he was a baby. And for many weeks and months his only food consisted of milk. He was not able to deliver speeches for many, many weeks. In fact, he could not even walk. And then finally, when he reached the age of let us say nine months, he started to walk. Now, what is wrong with this biography? It stresses the common. All babies are this way, but a biography is supposed to stress the uncommon — the extraordinary. If I were to tell you that after Napoleon was born and when only three days old he exclaimed, "Mother, give me a gun." That would be interesting.

What is Common and What is Uncommon

The two essential patterns are to look for phenomena which we have in common, and to look for what is uncommon or unique about a phenomenon. If you would like my opinion about a person and I say, "He is a human being like any other human being," that is no answer. You want to bring out what is special about him. This is an essential way of describing human beings. Now let me not be one-sided and say that this is the only way. We also have to know what all human beings have in common. While lungs are more or less the same in all bodies, no two human beings have the same face. I have often been told by people, "I know someone who looks like you." I would love to meet him because no two human beings look exactly alike. This is a mystery my friends. It indicates the uniqueness of a person.

It is comparatively easy to establish what we call features which human beings have in common, but it is very difficult to come upon what is unique about a person. It is so difficult really to describe a face. Natural science is concerned essentially with what is commonness of phenomena. The task of the humanities is to stress what is unique about a situation.

Now we need a definition of man. We need to talk about man. How do you talk about man? I would like to deliver a bit of an attack on much thinking, including my own. We are all inclined to think about man in non-human terms. I hate to be blasphemous, but have you ever heard the term "manpower?" What interests me at the moment is not the moral aspect but the cognizant aspect of it. It is just not right to speak about man in non-human terms. My dream is to learn to speak about man in human terms. Let me give you an example.

A famous person made the following statement. "Nature keeps

a human orchard healthy by pruning. War is the pruning hook."
Therefore war is a good thing. Now, what is the fallacy of this?
I am not discussing the morality of it. The fallacy is that we are
talking about society — humanity — as if it were an orchard. There
is a difference. I am speaking now strictly in a critical manner. We
have to learn to speak about man according to the human manner
because man is man. It is a very common statement that war is a
biological necessity, but man is more than biology. He is a biological entity but much more. I would like to say that while we have
a great many sciences dealing with man like anthropology, economics, linguistics, etc., there is really no science dealing with the
humanity of man. The result is that we do not understand our own
situation nor do we understand society in the world at large. I
would say then that we must try to listen carefully to that which
comes out of our existence.

Who Is Man?

The meaning of "human being" is much more than just being.
Let us explore it. It is true we know a great deal about man. It is
also true that our basic image of man is still under question. Is it
not conceivable that our entire civilization is built upon misin-
terpretation of man? I believe you saw a short fragment of an
article of mine dealing with the problem where I criticize the fact
that most essays on man are usually entitled, "What Is Man?"
Whenever you say "what" you refer to a thing, but man is not
a thing. He is a person. The right question would be "Who Is Man?"
rather than "What Is Man?"

The formulation of a question is the first step — like the saying,
"A good question is half the answer." The moment you ask "What
Is Man?" you have already put man in the realm of thinghood.
A theory of things does not shape and determine the things, but
a theory of man shapes and determines man. Man is what he
thinks he is.

We can only think of man if we care for man. I hope you do not
think this is a dogma. This is true. We can only think of and understand man if we have love for man. A concern for the understanding
of man is not something to be delegated. When it comes to an issue

54

like, "Who Is Man?," I know that just as I had to go through childhood, adolescence and maturity, I must go through the crisis, heartaches, embarrassments and wrestlings with this very issue. I cannot delegate this meditation and search to anybody else.

I would like to stress this care for man because it seems to be a principle easily forgotten. Namely, one cannot study the condition of man without being touched by the plight of man. Biologically, man is intact, still he is essentially afflicted with a sense of helplessness, discontent and fear. Outwardly, *Homo sapiens* may pretend to be satisfied and strong and inwardly they are poor, needy, vulnerable, always on the verge of misery, prone to suffer mentally, and physically. Just scratch his skin and you come upon bereavement, affliction, uncertainty. Man is so easily offended.

The definition of man is an old problem in the history of humanity. It was of great concern in the Bible, very much a concern in Greek philosophy and is of concern today. Another problem current today is the dehumanization of man — an activity in which many of us may be actively involved. We must face the prospect that this earth may be populated with a race of beings which though belonging to the race of *Homo sapiens* according to biology, will be devoid of the qualities by which man is spiritually distinguished. To be human we must know what being human means and how to acquire and preserve this knowledge. This requires tremendous effort and it is the most urgent issue we face. Just as death is the liquidation of a human being, dehumanization is the liquidation of being human.

A human being is a disclosure of the Divine, if I am allowed to quote in a religious spirit. The pagans had symbols, images, icons. If one goes to the Mediterranean islands, there are always statues. The Bible said no statues, no icons and no images — man! Right at the beginning of the Ten Commandments we find "Thou shall not make an image, or a likeness." At the same time, the Bible speaks of man as created in the image and the likeness of God. We have no symbols of God. According to the Hebrew prophets, a symbol of God is a desecration — a blasphemy. There is only one symbol of man — every man. You must not make a symbol. The task is to be a symbol.

In society, I am an average person. Yet I have never met the average person. There is no average person really. I am not an average person to myself. In the eyes of society I may be another human being, but in my eyes I am different. My existence is an original and not a copy. I think I have something to say — at least to myself. Every human being has that uniqueness. Do I not have a face? To my mind I am terribly precious. I am not an average person. I am exceedingly noteworthy to me, and it is the notability of my existence that becomes elusive when I look at myself from the point of view of society. But to me, my singularity is a matter of personal concern. In the eyes of the world, I repeat, I am an average man, but in my heart I am not an average man. I am a great deal more.

Being human means to go beyond sheer continuity — surprise. There is a singularity. Sheer continuity leads to the suspension of singularity, drudgery, inner devastation and demolition of all moments. Being human means to live through moments. No man is an average man. No life is really ordinary.

CHAPTER 5

Technology and the Integrative System

Kenneth E. Boulding, Ph.D.

**Professor of Economics
Michigan University**

History in general, and human history in particular, is a very complex pattern in four dimensions, three dimensions in space and one of time. The study of social dynamics attempts to find patterns in this structure which are repeated almost the way the patterns are repeated in wallpaper. If we can find such patterns then we have a fair chance of making predictions. If we can find stable relationships between things which we want to control and things which we cannot control we may be able to extend our area of control and actually mold the future rather than predicting it. We do this molding of the future every time we make a plan, for part of the determinants of the future is the image of the future which we have at the present.

This complex pattern in space-time that we call history is not homogeneous. It has, indeed, a structure which might be compared to a layer cake. A number of different social systems or patterns can be postulated, each of which has a certain dynamic of its own, in the sense that its own future is in part derived from its own past in a fairly regular, stable way, within which, also, each of these parallel systems affects the others. We might illustrate this in Figure 1 where the lines A, B and C represent three parallel systems. A, for instance, might represent the economic system, B the political system and C the religious system, each of which has a certain independence of its own as reflected by the horizontal arrows, but each of which also interacts with the others, as represented by the diagonal arrows, so the total process is a result partly of each system pursuing an independent course of its own, partly a result of each system acting upon others. Thus the process of economic development has a certain dynamic of its own in which the present character of the economy in regard to investments and the distribution of resources has a great deal to do with determining what the economy is going to be like next year or even in ten years. On the other hand, the economic system is always subject to influences from other systems, from the political system or from the religious system. A new government or a religious reformation may profoundly affect the development of the economy. Each of these other systems likewise has a certain integrity of its own, and it is likewise affected by the economy. The society which is having rapid economic development will find that both its political and its religious structure are profoundly affected by this fact.

Figure 1.

**Social systems as a parallel series
of interacting dynamic systems.**

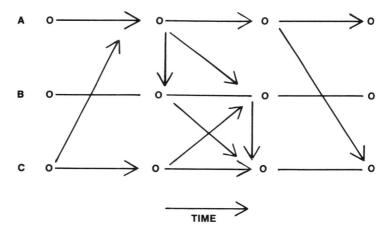

58

Exactly how we define the "layers" of the layer cake is to some extent arbitrary. The layers are not clearly defined in nature and at the edges especially they merge into each other so that it is certainly not easy to say, for instance, where the economic system ends and the political system begins. For purposes of analysis, however, it is useful to define certain broad areas of the social system as quasi-independent sub-systems and to discuss the interaction among them. This paper will concentrate on two of these sub-systems of great importance, both of which have a great deal of independence in the sense that the horizontal arrows of Figure 1 represent strong relationships and the future of each system is determined in considerable measure by its own past. Both systems also have very strong impacts each on the other. These two systems are the technological system and the integrative system. Neither of these is easy to define, especially at the edges; each of them however is a system with a good deal of independence.

The Technological System

The technological system is that aspect of society which is concerned with human artifacts both material and social and of the interactions of humans with artifacts, largely in the process of producing more artifacts. We think of technology in terms of tools, implements, machines and the ways of using them. We think of it also in terms of human skills, roles and organizations. A state, a church or a corporation is as much an artifact as a weapon, an altar or an account book. The history of technology is a history of the increasing complexity, variety and number of human artifacts, starting with primitive tools such as chipped flints, arrows and spears, early dwellings, clothing. We work up to agriculture, metallurgy, wheeled vehicles, ships, roads, domesticated animals, villages, cities and empires, money, credit and banking. This process finally leads in the present day to electrical and nuclear power, railroads, airplanes, computers, nuclear weapons, missiles, nation states and the United Nations.

As we define it, technology seems to include almost everything. Within this larger process of social evolution we want to distinguish material technology on the one hand and social technology on the other. Even material technology has a certain dynamic of its own.

59

We can treat human artifacts as if they were an evolutionary species with populations, birth rates, death rates, the birth of an artifact being its production and its death its consumption. Thus in the past 60 years the world has become largely populated with large four-wheeled metal bugs with detachable brains, called automobiles. These constitute a social species, with its own genetic apparatus: wombs in the shape of automobile factories; sperm in the shape of ideas in the heads of engineers; death in the form of final passage to an automobile graveyard; and even a certain amount of resurrection in the shape of spare parts and steel scrap. The mutation which produced the automobile has had a profound effect on the whole ecological system of the world and has altered the numbers of almost all other species both biological and social. It has diminished the number of horses, increased the number of supermarkets, increased the areas devoted to roads, increased peculiar roadside vegetation, altered the pattern of forest fires, polluted the atmosphere and increased the lead content of the top level of the oceans by several orders of magnitude. The automobile, furthermore, is a good example of the inner dynamic of material technology. It could not possibly have been developed much earlier than it was, for at least 200 inventions had to precede it, such as the vulcanization of rubber, the fractionation of oil, and so on. Once these inventions had been made it would have been hard to prevent the automobile. The fact that is so often noted in the history of technology that certain inventions are made quite independently by different people in different parts of the world at about the same time is a very clear proof of the independence of the dynamic of material technology, given a certain social climate and certain payoffs in the social system.

The Integrative System

What I call the "integrative system" is much less familiar than the technological system, for the idea that the integrative system exists at all is a fairly new one. Nevertheless I am prepared both to define and defend a "layer" of the total social system which deserves this name. The integrative system then is that part of the total social system which deals with such matters as status, community, identity, legitimacy, loyalty, love, respect, dignity,

60

acceptance and so on, and of course the negative aspects of these variables, alienation, hostility, exclusion, malevolence, hatred, disloyalty, illegitimacy and so on. In this country especially, we have not taken these aspects of social life very seriously. We have regarded them either as purely personal and eccentric, like young lovers in the park, or we have taken them for granted, and assumed, for instance, that power and wealth always creates its own legitimacy. This, I think, is a grave error, and contributes more than anything else to the frustration of our policies and the extremely unsatisfactory nature of our present political life. This is nowhere more evident than it is in Viet Nam where we are under the illusion that threat capability will create its own legitimacy whereas in fact it does not. With 10 times the military power that the French had in Viet Nam we find ourselves quite incapable of achieving the kind of stable, independent and democratic society that we desire, simply because we cannot achieve legitimacy, and the very extent of our power destroys any legitimacy we might have.

The Grants Economy

As a first approximation the integrative system may be defined in terms of extent and structure by what I have called the "grants economy." A grant is a unilateral transfer or sacrifice from one person or social unit to another, without anything passing in return. Exchange, by contrast, is bilateral transfer in which A gives something to B and B gives something to A. A grant or unilateral transfer from A to B can only take place if there is an integrative relationship between them; that is, if A in some sense identifies with B and regards him as being in the same community of interest with himself. When we give a dime to a beggar out of pity, there is a low level integrative relationship, the level, perhaps of common humanity, which is not very strong but which does exist. A study of the grants economy, even in money terms, would tell us a lot about the structure of the world integrative system. It would reveal, for instance, that the national state is by far and away the most powerful integrative system, for the grants which the state makes to its own citizens far exceed in magnitude any other grants. In most well organized and developed national states the internal grants of the state to its own citizens are at least of the order of

61

magnitude of 10 percent of the gross national product. Foreign aid is usually well below one percent of the gross national product. Internal charity and philanthropy, religious gifts and missionary endeavors and so on are not much more than this.

A study of the grants economy would further reveal the integrative weakness of many systems which make a good deal of show of integrative rhetoric. Class, for instance, is extraordinarily weak as an integrative system. The workers of the world do not unite. World socialism is very weak as an integrative system. The Russians, for instance, did practically nothing for the Chinese, in spite of the fact that they ostensibly had the same ideology so it is not surprising that the Chinese are so angry with the Russians! Here we have an example of where the inability of an ostensibly integrative system to create a grants economy in effect produced an integrative split. The Russian contribution to Chinese development was about one cent per Chinese per annum, and even this was in the form of a loan which the Chinese had to pay back when they were under particularly difficult circumstances. The Russians were prepared to do a good deal for the Uzbeks because Uzbekistan is in the same national state as the Russians; that is, the Soviet Union. They did virtually nothing for the Chinese and have actively exploited East Germany, in spite of the supposedly ideological community. The strongest national integrative system, as a matter of fact, was the old French Empire. The French gave a much larger proportion of their gross national product in foreign aid into their old Empire than any other country.

Grants in money or commodities are not of course the whole story, for there are many other forms of sacrifice, culminating of course in the sacrifice of life itself, which is the most extreme measure of an integrative relationship. "Greater love hath no man than this, that he lay down his life for his friend." Grants can also be made in the shape of time and energy and unpaid work. They may be measured indeed by "terms of trade" which are in some sense below normal. If people give a lot to something and get very little out of it, then presumably they are giving a grant and this is both a measure and a symbol of an integrative relationship. The dynamics of a system of this kind is often very peculiar. Sacrifices — to use a term which is more general than grants — are at the same time both the measure of an integrative relationship and also sometimes its cause. If we once start making sacrifices for something we find it very hard to admit to ourselves that the sacrifices have been in vain. Hence, sacrifices tend to be self-justifying in that they create the integrative system which justifies them and in the interests of which they are made. This is why the blood of the Martyrs is the seed of the Church and the blood of the soldiers the seed of the state. We feel that we cannot "let down" those who have made sacrifices in the past with whom we identify. The sacrifice of life has a peculiar emotional intensity, as the extreme magnitude of the integrative relationship, and it is not surprising that many sacred institutions have originated in human sacrifice. One thinks of the religion of the Aztecs, of Moloch, of the ancient Chinese burials, and their modern equivalent in the national state, which demands constant sacrifice of young men on the battlefield in order to maintain the love and the loyalty which people bear towards it. Moloch is not only one of the most ancient of gods, but one of the most persistent.

In the course of the development of the integrative system the discovery is always made that vicarious or substitutional sacrifice performs most if not all of the functions of real sacrifice. The victims in the graves of the monarchs of early civilizations are replaced by statues and figurines. Animal sacrifices and scapegoats replace the human sacrifices of ancient religions. The purely symbolic sacrifice of the Mass replaces even the animal sacrifices of the temple. Similarly, we may perhaps think of the development of foreign aid as the beginnings of substitutionary sacrifice in the national state and we may hope, perhaps, that as the national state as an institution matures the time will come when it will seem perfectly appropriate to sacrifice money for it but absolutely absurd and indecent to sacrifice human life the way we do today. It will then seem preposterous that anybody should be asked to die for his country, just as nobody is now asked to die for his religion or his lord.

The Unity of the Integrative System

We could spend a great deal more time in developing the concepts of the integrative system. Enough has been said, however, to suggest that it exists, that it is a social reality of great importance and that it has a certain unity of its own. Its internal dynamic produces a time pattern something like an escarpment. The origins of all integrative systems are obscure, but once they begin, however, they develop a dynamic of their own. Sacrifices which are made create a further sense of integration which enables the objects of these sacrifices to command still more sacrifices. These create a greater sense of integration with rising integrative relationship and rising sacrifices, until finally we reach the top of the system, until it is at the height of its power and extent and then frequently it collapses quite suddenly in a surprising debacle. The temples are suddenly deserted, the monarch is abandoned and the empire is destroyed. Sacrifice is piled on sacrifice until suddenly at some point it seems too much, and at that point the whole system collapses abruptly.

This pattern of cumulative unilateral sacrifice leading to collapse, however, is fortunately not the only pattern of the system. There is another pattern which might be described as reciprocity. Reciprocity is superficially like exchange and is often confused with it. It differs from exchange, however, in that whereas exchange is a conditional relationship reciprocity is unconditional. In exchange A gives something to B on the condition that B gives something to A, and vice versa. In reciprocity A gives something to B unconditionally whether B gives anything to A or not and similarly B gives something to A unconditionally whether A gives anything to B or not. Thus while we have mutual and bilateral transfers as in an exchange these transfers have the quality of grants or sacrifices which pure exchange does not. A very good example of reciprocity is the exchange of Christmas presents, which is a very important ritual in the reaffirmation of the integrative system of the family and the intimate friendship group, even though the terms of trade here are important. One who never gives any Christmas presents will pretty soon find that he doesn't get any. The fact that it is an exchange of gifts which is supposed to be unconditional is of great importance in creating the integrative affect. This is why an exchange of money, for instance, is much less satisfactory than an exchange of commodities in developing an integrative relationship. The growth of reciprocity, fortunately, does not follow the pathological pattern which the growth of

64

unilateral sacrifices is apt to do. It produces a pattern of healthy mutuality and equality of status whereas the pattern of sacrifice produces hierarchy, organizational schizophrenia and paranoia and eventually unstable organization. Thus, if we simply say, "Ask not what America will do for you, ask what you can do for your country," this is a symbol of a "sacrifice trap" which will eventually lead to too much sacrifice for the country and eventual collapse of the national integrative system. Suppose now we contrast our reactions to the phrase, "Ask not what General Motors can do for you, ask only what you can do for General Motors." We see the difference between an organization with a strong integrative system like the national state and an organization which is almost purely within the exchange system like a corporation.

The trouble with the corporation and indeed with almost all purely economic organizations is that everybody has good terms of trade with them. We do ask what General Motors can do for us and the answer is, "Quite a lot." If we are employed by it, it gives us good wages; if we buy from it, it gives us automobiles. As a result, however, of existing in a purely exchange environment it creates a very weak integrative system. One of the problems of General Motors is that nobody loves it much, hence it is ultimately very vulnerable to shifts in the integrative system which would deny it legitimacy. The only answer to this seems to be a system of reciprocity which combines the virtues of the exchange system, which are very great, with the development of an integrative structure. I am not suggesting that we should have Christmas all the year round but we do need to think about how we can introduce some of this element into the system. It may be, for instance, that the trading stamp is an interesting example of the introduction of something that looks like a Christmas present into a system which otherwise would be pure exchange.

In the case of the national state also, even though a citizen perhaps should not ask too loud and clear, "What can my country do for me?," the country should ask itself very loud and clear what it can do for its citizens. The whole meaning of democracy and the collapse of the legitimacy of morarchy and the absolute state rests upon the principle that a system of pure sacrifice is unstable and even the state must develop reciprocity. That is, the terms of trade

65

of a citizen with his country is a very important question, and how much he gets for what he gives is a highly legitimate social value. Even if we are not allowed to ask this ourselves, somebody should ask it for us. The whole theory of the democratic state indeed is that if the existing government does not provide good terms of trade for its citizens and gives them a good deal in terms of what they give to it, it should be voted out. On the other hand, it may also be that reciprocity is the real key to a healthy integrative relationship. Perhaps we should indeed give to our country unconditionally and it should give unconditionally to us.

There seems to be an almost inevitable paradox about reciprocity in the sense that even though the exchange of gifts is unconditional, the terms of trade in past exchanges is significant in determining the willingness of people to enter into future exchanges. If the terms of trade for any party to a reciprocal arrangement are bad and persistently bad, this may eventually destroy the integrative system on which the reciprocal relationship depends.

Interaction Between the Two Systems

The interactions between the technological system and the integrative system represented by the diagonal or even vertical arrows of Figure 1, are extremely complex and enormously important. We cannot hope to do more than hint at some of the possibilities here. The relations are profoundly reciprocal. The dynamic properties of the technological system depend in considerable degree on its integrative matrix, likewise the development of technology produces enormous effects on the system of loyalties, legitimacies, and affections. Here we can only illustrate some possible connections.

We tend to take the enormous technological dynamic of Western society in the last 300 years very much for granted. Nevertheless, it is one of the most puzzling phenomena in human history. Suppose we ask ourselves the question, for instance as Joseph Needham has done, why the great mutation into science and science-based technology took place in Europe and the Atlantic world and not in China? Up to the year 1600 there can be little doubt that China was the center of the human race. It was indeed the Middle Kingdom. Most of the important technological developments in the first 1600 years of the Christian era originated in China and arrived in Europe often some 300 years later. Eighteenth century European intellectuals regarded China as the most advanced, developed and civilized country in the world. The history of the last 300 years, however, has been written largely in terms of the fact that Europe made the breakthrough into modern science, whereas China did not, and is now desperately trying to catch up with this 300-year lag. The reasons for this difference are still very obscure, but many of them unquestionably lie in the nature of the integrative system in the two societies. It may well be that China was too well integrated to permit a revolution in knowledge. It was administered by a bureaucracy, recruited by public examination, and hence always open to able and ambitious young men, who could thus enter the system and become part of the establishment. There was really only one central power and one central loyalty. There was no separation of church and state. The magistrate performed the functions of the priest. A powerfully unified system of loyalty and affection was created with the study of the classics and the pursuit of Confucian ideals. This integrative system was powerful enough and integrated enough so that alternative systems, whether Christianity or Islam, could make no real headway against it. Buddhism and Taoism degenerated into purely popular religions, incapable of challenging the established order of the society.

Europe by contrast was deeply divided not only into separate nation states but divided as to church and state, with a long, early tradition of conflict between the Pope and the Emperor, and the further split caused by the Reformation and the Counter Reformation. The Roman Church might try to suppress Galileo, but what was impiety in one place could become piety in another. Hence in this fractured integrative system it was possible to develop a small sub-culture almost in the interstices of the fractures themselves. It was committed to veracity, without fear of novelty, liberated from the tyranny of intellectual authority, devoted to the testing of realities and to the reality and importance of the natural world. There are many puzzling aspects still of this phenomenon; nevertheless, it is clear that the nature of the integrative system had an enormous impact. China had an Un-Chinese Activities Committee for too long. It created too much loyalty, too much commitment to the established ways and established orders. In Europe disloyalty was easier. Luther was disloyal to the Pope;

the Prince was disloyal to the Emperor. There was indeed no universal loyalty and hence man's mind was free for loyalty to the truth which is the foundation of scientific advance.

Coming closer to our own day, we can see many cases in which the spread of the science-based technology is hampered by the nature of the integrative system of particular countries and societies. India is a strong case in point, where the traditional integrative system of the Indian village is enormously strong. In a caste society everybody has a place. Hence it is very hard to find a place for the innovator who indeed is often seen as a threat to the highly integrated established order. In India, indeed, it seems that innovation is largely confined either to those who have broken out of the established order through contact with Western education or to those who are refugees from Pakistan and hence have been forced out of their traditional established order. In Latin America again we see an integrative system which this time perhaps is too weak to create the matrix within which a successful transition to science-based technology can be achieved. Internal conflict and the inability to achieve any political synthesis in the society has led to rule by the military, which is rarely friendly toward technological development. Here again all generalizations should be looked on suspiciously, but the notion of an interaction between the integrative system and the technological system is of profound importance and needs much further study.

The Dynamics of Technology

On the other side, the dynamics of technology have a constant impact on the integrative system. Illustrations could be multiplied almost indefinitely. One looks, for instance, at what I have elsewhere called the "organizational revolution;" that is, the rise in the size of organizations of all kinds which began about 1870. This is directly related to certain technological changes in the system of communications — the telephone, the telegraph, the mimeograph, the dictaphone — and also certain social inventions, especially in the form of organization of the executive and the division of labor in bureaucracies. All this has permitted an enormous increase in the optimum size of the organization and has created such organizations as General Motors, the United Auto

68

Workers, the American Association for the Advancement of Science, the American Medical Association, the United States Department of Defense, the Soviet Union, and even the Metropolitan Life Insurance Company. This produces all sorts of change in the integrative system. The kind of loyalty which people have to a small organization is very different from what they have to a large one. The integrative system of a small family firm is very different from that of a large corporation. It is not surprising that as the size of the organization grows we see movement from status to contract, a movement perhaps from reciprocity towards contractual exchange. On the other hand, growth of organizations produces a profound change in the interrelations between them. We move from something like perfect competition into oligopoly, not only in the relations of firms but also in the relations of states. This profoundly affects the nature of the structure of legitimacy.

The technological revolution in communications, as McLuhan has suggested, is producing an enormous impact, not only on forms of organization but on the whole spirit and structure of society including the whole nature of the learning process, which is the most fundamental process in all social dynamics. The development of television, for instance, which can be regarded on the whole as pure offshoot of the dynamics of technology, has had an enormous effect on all aspects of human life: on the family, on politics, on the nature of rhetoric, on drama and the arts and on formal education. It upsets traditional societies everywhere and has played a large part in creating this remarkable generation of young people which we now have with us, who have been raised all their lives on TV. By introducing, as it were, a competitive source of information into the home to the parents, it produces profound changes in psychological development. We are certainly going to have to rewrite psychoanalysis as a result of the TV set. It destroys the intimacy of the local or even the national community and moves us a long way towards the "spaceship earth," which is such a remarkably apt symbol of the world to come.

Another illustration of the impact of technology on the integrative system is the enormous impact of the automobile. Here again we have something which came mainly out of technological evolution which has profoundly changed the structure of our cities, the nature of the family, the nature of human intercourse, even the structure of retailing. Even after 60 years of experience of what it has really done to us hardly anybody knows. In a very real sense it has destroyed the city as an integrative system. It has intensified the class structure at one end of the scale while it has destroyed classes at the other end. It has helped create a society with a very large middle class and a very intractable small poverty sub-culture. It has changed the nature of crime and police. It has affected the birth rate and has tended to destroy both the bachelor and the extended family. The principal unit of social behavior is now the nuclear family that can fit into a car.

Military technology has had an enormous impact on the structure of the international system. Probably the most important agent in destroying the feudal system was gunpowder. The terms of trade of the baron with his retainers became too unfavorable for the retainers once gunpowder was invented and the baron could offer them no real protection. In a very real sense, therefore, gunpowder led to the destruction of feudal loyalties and the rise of loyalties to the national state. It seems highly probable that the development of the nuclear weapon and the missile with a range of half the earth's diameter will do for the national state what gunpowder did for the feudal baron. It makes it only conditionally viable from a military point of view and this in the long run will destroy its sacred character. When it becomes clear that your country can do nothing for you in the way of defending you, the question of why you should do anything for it becomes perfectly sensible and it is quite possible that the national state in the next 100 years or so will go the way of the monarchy and the empire, in the sense that if it is to retain its legitimacy it will have to abandon its power, that is, its threat capability. Paradoxical as it may seem, unilateral disarmament may be the only really adequate method of national defense. All this again results essentially from the impact of technology on the integrative system and again all propositions in this area must be regarded as highly tentative. All we can be sure of is that the impacts will be large.*

The impact of scientific technology on religion is another area in which a good deal has been written but on which not very

---

* I have deliberately avoided the problem of automation and the impact of computers, mainly because so much has been written on it and so little is known about it!

much is known. It is clear, of course, that the scientific image of the universe has profoundly affected religious ideologies in regard to cosmology and even in regard to ethics and the nature of man himself. Dante may well have half believed in the geography of hell and of purgatory. We now know, however, that at least purgatory is not at the South Pole, because we have been there. The Copernican Revolution profoundly destroyed the old cosmology of the Christian Church, the old three-story universe, with hell in the basement, earth on the first floor and heaven in the attic. Similarly, the impacts of modern medicine have forced a profound revision in religious teaching in regard to sex and birth control. Death control and birth control indeed are part of the same package. The scientific point of view, furthermore, by introducing historical criticism of the sacred books and by its general elevation of empirical testing over traditional authority, has had a corrosive effect on totalitarian religion. Nevertheless religion has survived all these adversities and shows no signs at all of disappearing. In the United States, church membership is at an all time high, with some 64 percent of the population, and has risen fairly steadily for nearly 200 years. In Europe it is Christian democracy that picked up the pieces after the collapse of fascism. Even in the socialist countries the church exhibits astonishing vitality and the moderate persecution to which it has been subjected seems to have purified it. In Japan there have been many new religions in the last 100 years and new forms of Buddhism in particular are showing great vitality. All this may seem very surprising to those who are still in the age of 18th century enlightenment, as so many intellectuals are, but it is a fact of the world that has to be taken into account and is evidence of the extraordinary ability of religion to adapt itself to the implications of technological and scientific change.

Status and Contract

It should be clear that these interactions are so complex that anyone who offers a single key to them is likely to be faced with the fact that there are far too many locks to open and that no single key will fit them all. Sir Henry Maine, for instance, saw the great movement of history as one leading from a society of status to one of contract, that is, a society in which roles were assigned mainly through the integrative system to one in which roles are assigned largely through exchange. There is, of course, something in this view, especially as we contemplate the rise of capitalism and the decline of feudalism.

The rise of the insurance industry itself is a very interesting example of this principle. In what my children call the "olden days," in which they think I was born, the only insurance policy was one's status in the integrative system as a parent or as a monk or as a feudal retainer. Today the formalization of insurance has largely replaced status as the principle method of providing for accidents and old age. Nevertheless, the rise of socialism, not only in socialist countries themselves, but in the development of the welfare state in the capitalist world, is a reflection of a certain breakdown in the exchange mechanism and to some extent a return to status. The Social Security contract is of a slightly different order from that which we have with a private insurance company. It arises out of our status as citizens in a society, not as a contract with a private organization. The "retreat," if indeed it is, from contract back to status, which we see in the socialist countries is even more striking. An enormous appeal has to be made to the solidarity of the individual with the society and to his concern for the future, if more naked forms of coercion are to be avoided in getting at the product. Socialism indeed is an interesting example of the extraordinary difficulties of integrative development. It arises as an ideology in large measure out of protest against what are perceived to be the inequities of the system of pure exchange. Also out of a yearning for a society in which people did things for love rather than for money, in which the grubbiness of trade was replaced by the altruism of unselfish service and in which, as it were, the whole of society became one big happy family. Unfortunately, abolishing the market and free exchange and the private property on which these stand does not automatically create an integrative society. The history of socialist societies is a grim illustration of how the search for larger integration can easily lead into a retreat into coercion as the grim record of Stalinism, or the even grimmer record of Hitler testifies. Even National Socialism was a search for an integrative system, however nationalistic and exclusive, and was motivated by some of the same dissatisfactions with liberal capitalism which gave rise to communism.

I have done little more in this paper than to suggest an enormous field of inquiry. We know very little about the integrative system, even less than we know about the dynamics of technology, and we do not even know very much about that. I am convinced, however, that it is precisely in the interaction of these two great dynamic systems that the understanding of the main dynamics processes of society must lie. In this country we are fairly sensitive to the dynamics of technology. We are, however, extraordinarily insensitive to the dynamics of the integrative system. We have something that might be called integrative policy in, for instance, racial policies, educational policies, and the bare beginnings of an integrative policy in the international system, through such things as cultural exchange. We do not, however, have any clear concept of the integrative system as a whole. I have been trying to persuade people for many years that we should study love just as seriously and intensely as we study anything else. This suggestion is usually met with jeers. We seem to be thoroughly indoctrinated with the view that anything which is preached about cannot be taken seriously. We may never make a costlier mistake, and all our technological and economic success may go down the drain if it produces a society which is incapable of love, incapable of attracting an uncoerced loyalty and incapable of establishing or maintaining its own legitimacy.

CHAPTER 6

The City and the Human Being

August Heckscher

Chairman
The Twentieth Century Fund

"The State was made for man, not man for the State." Thus does the conservative orator traditionally invoke the supremacy of the human cause — often, it must be said, to deny the very things that would make human life a little more pleasant and secure. The phrase is nevertheless a good one; it is even better, in present circumstances, if we change it a little and say: "The *city* was made for man, not man for the city." It falls then with a fresh relevance, and indeed with a certain novelty.

We think of our cities from several points of view, as being made for manufacture and trade, or made for transportation, or even made for the arts. We rarely think of them as having been made — specifically and deliberately — for man. Indeed man himself, whether in the rich countries of the industrialized world or the poor and swollen metropoli of the underdeveloped southern half of the globe, must be generally surprised to hear it said that the noisy streets through which he walks in peril, and the stuffy crowded quarters where he lives, were conceived and created for his benefit alone. He must rather feel like a creature that has taken possession of an unfriendly environment, and is by some miracle managing to survive there.

In the springtime of our civilization, when cities were new, Aristotle put the matter in the right way. Man, he said, is "a community-building animal." At the very start of his book on politics, in the first tremendous sentence of that tremendous work, he proclaimed that man is the creator of the social and physical environment in which he lives. A later, wearier age would have been content to say merely that man is a city-*dwelling* animal — one which exists passively, sometimes not too unhappily, almost always somewhat dazed and beaten, in a world that somebody else made.

It is my purpose to look at the modern city in terms of what it means and can mean for the human being. This is a crucial matter, for the human being hereafter, whether he likes the idea or not, will inescapably be a city man. Even in the United States, where the myth of a rural utopia haunted for so long the minds of our literary men and of our politicians, the realization has dawned that we are destined to find the good life in cities, or else not find it at all. Our art deals almost completely with the complexities and the swift tempo of urban life; our politics at last adjust themselves to facts which should have been plain a long while ago. We are ending the long disenfranchisement of the city man; we are looking to the individuals who manage our great cities as potential leaders on the national scene. The Federal government adjusts itself slowly to today's realities. We have finally a Department of Urban Affairs — even though the Congress in its wisdom has not yet contrived a committee structure which reflects this new condition.

More striking than what is happening before our eyes is what is happening in economically backward countries. One would suppose that these would pass through a long period of agricultural development before they gathered together the population and resources upon which the great city depends. Quite the contrary seems to be the case. The people of the poorest countries flee the land, and crowd into cities long before economic conditions are ripe to sustain them. The economic history of Western Europe was the history of peoples gradually coalescing into ever-bigger communities; and the rise of towns heralded the new age of commerce, discovery and social progress. Today in the poor lands this process is reversed; or rather it ceases to be a process at all.

As there are people in the world who are familiar with the airplane yet have had no experience with intermediate forms of transportation, so there are vast millions who know the patterns of advanced city life without having passed through the stages of village and town. The great city attracts them all. Everywhere it is the existence to which the human being aspires — the prophecy of how man should live henceforth upon this planet.

Is the City Made for Man?

It is time we asked whether the city is in fact made for man.

A first response must necessarily be largely negative. Slums exist everywhere, except in a few of the smaller countries of northern Europe, and are an affront to humanity to a degree seldom fully recognized. We tend to look upon these slums as aberrations; we close our eyes to them as successfully as the wartime Germans closed theirs to the obscenities of Buchenwald or Auschwitz. Yet it is here that millions of our own people, supposedly the most favored of all people, live out their span in a state of brutal deprivation; and their children continue in the same grim cycle. We have now families unto the third generation living on welfare, caught in an environment from which there seems no escape.

We have heard so often about resolves to clear away the slums. My own grandfather launched a crusade to this end — one man with one man's hopelessly inadequate resources. Today the Federal government is in theory dedicated to the same end. Yet the untold wealth and power of the government seems no more able to deal with the problem than a single brave but quixotic individual. Until we address ourselves seriously to eliminating slum conditions, there is no use talking about the city as being made for man.

Only when one has said this, and said it in words as plain and loud as possible, does it seem right to go on to a discussion of the more subtle ways in which the city denies and thwarts life. Yet these subtle ways are not insignificant, and in the end their toll may be almost as great as the obvious assaults which slum conditions make upon decency and humaneness. There is hardly a city in this country today which does not crush man and belittle him. The journey to work is enough to unfit the individual for anything genuinely free or creative. The day spent in the city is devoid of most of those influences which refresh and enliven the spirit. In Washington, D. C., watch the government workers make their way into the subterranean cafeteria when the hour of the midday meal arrives; in New York, see them rush out into streets from which all humanizing elements have been eliminated. On Park Avenue, which is the center of the most spectacular concentration of new office buildings, hardly a serviceable shop or eating place exists; the pretty stenographer can find at best a bank or an automobile showroom, or can satisfy her desires only if she wishes to buy a bathtub or a Mosler safe. Those who may stay after hours for the entertainment which the city traditionally offers, battle their way through traffic to theatres which, for the most part, form part of one of the city's most degrading quarters, the home of the pervert and the panderer, the center for pornography and cheap sensationalism.

At noonday, in all weathers, passing the famous Seagram Building of Mies van der Rohe and Philip Johnson, one sees crowds clustering in the area formed by the building's setback. It is a touching sight, a hint of the use to which people would put an urban architecture truly conceived for their delight. But it is significant that these two great architects have eschewed almost everything which might invite the soul of the city man. There is water, to be sure — two wonderful fountains which pour out with enthusiasm a seemingly inexhaustible flow. Yet there are no benches — the people crawl precariously along the edge of the pools formed by the fountains, and perch uneasily upon the marble coping. There is little in the way of shade. Only the open space itself at the base of the noble building gives a hint of what might have been had the city been really built for man.

The foregoing remarks focus upon the public places and streets of the city: what shall we say of the places where people live? There is little to say, except that the spirit of the slums seems to have escaped the poorer and more sordid regions to infect men's ideas of what the human habitation should be, even in the most favorable circumstances.

In New York again (I cite New York not only because I live there but because it cannot help but be the standard-setter for great cities everywhere), there are acknowledged slums on Park Avenue north of 96th Street; south of the dividing line there are slums in spirit and in essence, notwithstanding the fact that they are inhabited by some of the richest people in the world. The broad avenue is devoid of variety of spatial excitement; it is shorn of the details which might give it charm or affirm the human scale. The buildings look into monotonous reflections of themselves; more often the back apartments, or the back rooms of even the most grandiose, look into blank walls and dark alleys.

Down the center of this avenue there is to be seen the most touching and the most pathetic evidence of man's lost dream that anywhere could be imagined. Here a private citizen of generosity and goodwill annually plants an array of flowers changing with the seasons. These flowers grow behind an iron fence. The traffic roars past the greater length of these sad plantations which create gardens that cannot be viewed except from a distance or from above — flowers whose scent is lost among the fumes of gasoline, and whose silence is mocked by the tumult around them.

This gift of color, this poor token of what should mark and grace a city, is praised and appreciated by the citizenry. So touchingly do they keep a feeling for what the city ought to be.

If we speak thus of the finest and most expensive street in the world, what shall we say of the more ordinary housing in the city? Most of it would be at home in Moscow — and that is the best and the worst that I can say. Anyone who drives from the airport in Moscow to the center of the city must be enormously impressed by the scenes of building activity; the cranes against the sky look like a new generation of giant beasts. He must also be depressed by the lack of human value in the housing which is being constructed. The workmanship may be a little shoddier, but the concept is certainly no more defiantly anti-human than what may be observed by anyone driving, say, up Bruckner Boulevard in The Bronx. These faceless buildings, rising from a barren land to touch a vacant sky, are the denial of everything which men, women and children have sought through history for the place in which their lives are spent.

Building Height

I digress at this point to say a word about height in buildings. It was once believed that to go up in height was to enhance human experience. The word skyscraper, as G. K. Chesterton remarked, is pure poetry, a beautiful exaggeration with something of the quality of the traditional American tall tale. It is almost as romantically descriptive as the phrase "a flight of stairs." The kind of building to which men had given so glorious a name was thought to be an answer to their need to escape the muddy atmosphere of earth, an ascent into the empyrean where there should be quiet, and natural vistas, and clean air. We still keep this idea, but the reality has resulted in a sad parody.

The grime of the city, its noise and the pollution of its atmosphere, do not cease as one goes upward; actually they seem to increase. More significantly, the lift of the spirit which men had anticipated all too rarely occurs. Nothing is more desolate than to look out upon nothing from the window of a tall building; if the experience is prolonged, it induces the mood of boredom and alienation which is all too characteristic of modern man wherever he may be. What counts from any promontory is the landscape which is given one to look at — the landscape or the skyscape. At their happiest, the tall buildings of today look out upon the tops of other tall buildings, thus restoring to the viewer some sense of the human scene. In the Chase Manhattan Building in New York, for example, one has the almost indescribable delight, upon emerging from the elevator, of looking out from the 65th floor through broad, floor-to-ceiling windows — upon what? Upon the tower of a lesser skyscraper built some 50 years ago. That tower, lovingly detailed and elaborated, hangs like a piece of sculpture in the sky, and gives to the bay and the city stretching around a quality rarely sensed before.

What happens more often, unfortunately, is that the tall building looks out upon the blank wall of an even taller building which has just been put up or (more tantalizingly) is in the very process of being constructed, cutting off the view and air one had risen so far to seek. Most of the tall buildings in New York make no esthetic sense at all, for they provide at the 30th or 40th story almost exactly the same outlook that one could have gained a few stories above the street. The room where I have written these lines is on the sixth story; and here, by a happy chance, some of the true quality of the urban skyscape has been preserved. I look over gables and chimney pots to the south, where the tall buildings of mid-Manhattan take off for their dramatic leap into the upper airs.

As far as ordinary living is concerned, and ordinary families, height is a bitter delusion. The mother at her chores is cut off by a maddening distance from the children playing below. The elevator rides are tedious and mechanical failure becomes a harrowing frustration. The views offer little in the way of compensation: at best they look into nothingness; at worst into an adjoining building. No wonder the lower floors are considered the most desirable by families in the newer housing developments. How delightful, in comparison to endless dependence on the elevator, must seem the old-fashioned access to the outdoors, through a door or down a few flight of stairs!

I end this digression with the observation that height in buildings can be, and often is, a factor detrimental to man; or at least that height per se is detrimental. What is needed in a city built for human beings is a reconsideration of the uses of height. Since buildings must obviously go upward to take care of an ever-increasing population upon a finite earth, we should ask to what uses the higher levels may best be put, and how they can be employed with the least harm to the people who live and work in them. Earth, not the sky, remains man's true home, and closeness to it continues a source of strength. As part of the re-evaluation now overdue, architects and planners must begin thinking creatively about the higher levels of their constructions, with the placing of towers and terraces being held as important to the sense of man's well-being as hills and valleys below. The monolithic shaft reaching a hundred or more stories into the sky is contrary to all that is agreeable and human in urban living.

I was speaking of housing as a test of the city's livability; it is perhaps unnecessary that I should say more in order to make my point. Places to live, places to work, places to learn, to shop, to enjoy the arts and celebrations of urban life — these make the city; and besides these the city is made by the means available for moving readily between these points — the walkways and streets through which we pass on foot, the connecting channels for public and private transportation. To analyze each of these would be to catalogue the discomforts and frustrations which afflict most city-dwellers. I would prefer to try a more positive approach, speaking of the role which the city should play in expanding human sensibility and enlarging men's sense of enjoyment and discrimination. For in the long run it is not enough that we should try to remove what bothers or distorts us. It is necessary that we acquire an understanding of the role which the environment — particularly the urban environment — should play in the making of man.

What Do We See?

I urge upon you, first, a realization of how stunted most of us become — how little we see of the world around us, how little we feel and truly observe. Most of us, indeed, go through life half dead. To a degree this deadness is an armor deliberately put on to protect us against the worst of the encroachments and defilements which are imposed upon us by modern conditions. Continuous noise is made bearable because we have learned not to listen; assaults upon the visual sense are tolerated because we have become blind. I once worked in a particularly unblessed part of the city: returning there now, I wonder how I could have daily put up with the surroundings. The answer, of course, is that I had mercifully found protection through insensitivity. But how much we lose through the putting on of this cloak, and how much are we less than whole human beings while we wear it!

Occasionally the senses are awakened, and then for a short time we have the excitement of living once more in a world where we see, hear and feel. To travel is to have one's mind made alive; the cities we pass through stand forth as if carved out of light. Men in the midst of great danger, even in an age when technology has dulled so many of his natural gifts, can find again what seemed to have been lost. A naval officer told me recently how in the last war the vessel he commanded made its way without instruments into harbors of the Pacific unknown and uncharted. Some talent for hearing and smelling, some lost sense of direction and a feeling for the nearness of things, guided them safely through. Afterwards, with charts available and such new instruments as radar at their disposal, these men found it inconceivable that they had found their way by the use of their own eyes and ears.

The immediate surroundings thus disappear from the view of

the modern city man; so also does a feeling for time and its passing. When sensations crowd with sufficient remorselessness upon us, we are aware of that only which impinges at the moment: what has come before and what will come after, the whole sense of time as a stream and a progression, vanishes from our consciousness. In my own experience, when life in the great city becomes intense, I notice that I tend completely to wash away the image of the previous day; sometimes a week or more will pass by before some stray word or glimpse reminds me of an encounter which should have been constantly in mind and indeed subtly altered everything that came after.

> Sorrowful dreams remembered after waking
> Shadow with color all the candid day . . .

So the poet affirms; but for most of us in modern life the dreams we have, whether sorrowful or joyful, fade before the onrush of an ever-new sensation.

In the best moments of life this cannot be so. Then we are aware of the subtleties of our environment, and we are aware of the past that has made us what we are. In his war memoirs Churchill has described how, after taking power in the crisis of 1940, all his past became alive. It was, he tells us, as if everything he had ever known, all he had learned and experienced and done, were awake and potent, guiding his every action in the present. How much dead stuff, by contrast, do most of us drag around in the day's work: all the baggage of our life that might, if we could but unpack and use it, warm us and cheer us in our tasks.

Now architecture has a role in awaking man and restoring his senses. The city, said Plutarch, is the teacher of man. It is also — or at least it should be — man's spiritual awakener. At the Twentieth Century Fund we are making an inquiry into research in the field of the Human Potential: what is being done to make man more aware and more sensitive, to enlarge his capacities for seeing and hearing and feeling what is around him. Many disciplines are now combining, in different parts of the country, to explore this wide area of human research. The architect and planner have their roles, I suggest, along with the psychologist, the educator, the therapist, the philosopher, and the seer. A city that is built for man is built to keep him at the highest level of his being.

The arts that are an essential part of any city — indeed that seem sometimes to be its chief reason for being — do of course have the effect of extending man. Painting, literature, music, the theatre and dance have from time out of mind had this role, making us see in life qualities which everyday existence tends to hide, restoring color and depth to the human comedy around us. Now what can be done by the art of city-building itself?

In a thousand seemingly unnoticed and unfelt ways the city stimulates our senses and illumines our vision. The way the light falls, the way a vista is open or is bounded, the contrast between natural and man-made things — these are among the teachers of man. The different surfaces under foot, the different degrees of enclosure overhead, the entrances and exits that mark our passages, the points that arrest us and the spaces that release us. And then the details of the city: its signs and lights, its shops and its benches, the movement of men and things, and the movement of such natural forces as winds and rivers . . . indeed, everything around us becomes part of an influence subtly shaping man and giving form and substance to his spirit.

The discouraging thing, of course, is how little the average city dweller actually sees. The average country dweller, for that matter, probably does not see all that there is in *his* landscape — the seasons pass with only a fraction of their drama touching him, and amid stars and flowers unnamed and unknown. But man over the ages has acquired an instinctive feeling for natural things, and learns to discriminate among them. The city, being comparatively new in history, lacks for him this innate familiarity. And so we should begin, I believe, to teach young people early and systematically what they should look for in the urban environment — what kind of aesthetic and sensual appetites it can be expected to satisfy.

A New Course

Every schoolchild should have a course based upon an appraisal of the physical aspects of the city, including a critical survey of his own community. How does it look from afar, seen as the traveler approaches it, with its particular skyline and its unique relationship to the terrain on which it stands? How does one enter it? The fact that cities and communities have entrances has been almost wholly lost sight of — which is probably one reason why the approach to most cities is sordidly ugly. (Contrast the gates of the old city with the longitudinal slum through which the individual passes on his way from the airport to the center of New Orleans — or of Seattle!) Once within the city, what are its focal points — the *joints* which mark a change of speed and direction or method of conveyance; the *magnets* which draw men and make the journey seem worth while? Have these been given form, so as to be discernible within the cityscape? Have the greater and the lesser elements of urban life been clearly marked out? Have the private and public places of the city been brought into a harmonious relationship?

Again — and by no means least important — are the past and the present in balance? I spoke earlier of the need to keep a sense of time's passing; and the city should be a teacher in this regard more constant in its influence than any philosopher. Most cities of today appear to have been struck off at one blow, as if man had not lived on the planet before yesterday. The conservation of man-made things is no longer a cause to be taken up by sentimentalists and antiquarians; it has its appeal to all who try to keep sanity in their lives, as well as to those who know that to design and build in a vacuum is an unrewarding assignment.

Every city has much that is worth saving; not all of it will be beautiful by any current standards — some will have a scale that needs desperately to be kept if we are not to be swallowed up by mere hugeness; some will have upon them the marks of the values of an earlier day. For the young people of a community to be able to see the importance of such scale and such values, for them to be able to discern the ages of the things around them, and their meanings and their embodied hopes, is to become wise as men and women, no less than as city dwellers.

Then there are more elusive qualities of the city which young people should learn in such a course as I have been envisioning: the nature of community, the things that create among the city's population a feeling of common ways and make possible continuing dialogue from which agreement upon fundamentals evolves. I am constantly impressed by how little even the most confirmed city dweller reflects upon these qualities. They see a street widened, or converted to one-way traffic, and note approvingly that the cars move more rapidly. They miss entirely the main point: the fact that the conditions which foster intercourse and shopping have been inevitably damaged.

Avenues which become a channel for through traffic soon lose their character as places; they are like a landscape through which a swollen river has passed. The motion of the waters erodes the banks, disturbs the quiet harmony of the shores, and soon drives away the fishermen and other folk who once had loved the scene. So a shopping district, a gathering place in a city, can all too quickly find its life curtailed. The sidewalks are eaten away first, as the demands of through traffic are ever more imperious. Then in ways less easily observed, the habit of moving about on foot is impaired (how can one enjoy walking among the fumes and the noise, when crossing back and forth becomes a threat to existence?) and the whole civilized tradition of casual meeting and conversations in the street is undermined.

I have seen the widening of a street successfully opposed because it would involve the chopping down of old trees. People understand trees, and on the whole they like them. But the atmosphere and conditions which give the street its character are rarely discerned or defended. They cannot be, because the people have never been taught to understand these things.

Similarly, the city dweller has little understanding of the shaping of outdoor places. On the whole they like open space within the city; but they do not realize how meaningless and vacant this becomes unless the space is controlled and shaped. Again, the comparison with water is apt. If water is not held in check, confined and released in some artful way, it becomes a barren flood. Space within the city is likewise meaningless except as it is given form. The typical open space in an American city, with its holes where space leaks out, its low densities of use and its disproportionately broad expanses of asphalt, is totally unfit for human enjoyment. Yet we have squares that once were models of civic charm. The courthouse squares of county seats across this country could well be made a subject for study and restoration. We might then be in a position to understand how, on an infinitely larger scale, in the conditions imposed by huge population and the complex movements of traffic, we could create the places that distinguish the true city from the urban jungle.

In such a course as I have spoken of, I would like to see stress placed also upon the need to create an effective transition between the city itself — the entity with its own being and limits — and the world outside. "Dear children," I would say, "here is our problem for today: Men and women must be able to come quickly and conveniently into this place where you live. But in so doing they must not destroy the place." I am certain that the children would come up with some better ideas for meeting the problem than our highway engineers and city planners have heretofore produced.

Not a city in this country has solved the problem of combining easy access with the preservation of civility. Boston lies broken apart by the steel and concrete structures which cross and recross it. San Francisco stands cut off from its bay, and Hartford from its river. The beautiful old section of New Orleans, the Vieux Carré, is threatened with having a wall built between its small-scale houses and the Mississippi from which it has drawn its life and its historic character. Seattle, so exquisitely placed upon the natural scene, sees its internal life brutally trampled upon by those who put a higher value on going through the place than on enjoying it once they have arrived.

A generation which had learned from youth the meaning of the city, to appreciate what is human and unique within it, would be in a position to express itself upon issues which touch them far more closely than most of those which now agitate our politics. Some of them might even become architects or planners themselves. And judging by what one sees upon the face of the American continent, they would know a few things which the architects and planners of the generation before them have scarcely glimpsed.

In the end it is to men that we must look if we are to build the city shaped to man's needs. A public aware of qualities which they now cannot articulate; a professional corps lifted above technical or even aesthetic knowledge to an understanding of the human condition; a political leadership able to see things worth doing in our midst at least as important as the exploration of space or the pursuit of foreign wars — from these will come a new civic structure. The chance of its coming may seem remote. But until their achievement — until the day dawned upon their realization — remoteness has always seemed to mark man's hopes.

CHAPTER 7

The Person and His Political Environment

Richard N. Goodwin

**Fellow, Center for Advanced Studies
Wesleyan University**

This Conference shares in the most representative intellectual current of the age: a passionate obsession with the individual. In literature and drama, philosophy and religion the constant infolding debate about the nature and existence of the individual person continues. Even if the argument ends in absurdity few artists can resist imparting a touch of nobility to the man who lives absurdly, though the absurdity was not of his creation. Thus Beckett's *Waiting for Godot* is partially a sentimental sham drawing us toward the central figures with an affection resting on their own qualities as well as our own similarities to them. This discourse has largely replaced the more familiar battles over ideologies, systems of values, and moral imperatives which are the stuff of so much Western history.

We are learning a great deal from this dialogue, and perhaps it will point direction toward a more satisfactory context for modern existence. It is also, however, a sure sign that the individual is in trouble. For doubt is the spur to debate; and we have placed the existence and the idea of man, as a moral and a significant being, in serious question.

My discussion is limited to the question of the individual and politics, a very narrow field. Yet it is impossible to discuss this question without reference to the wider content of society and thought from which politics, the most responsive of all activities to shifting conditions, takes its coloration and direction.

By politics I mean the process of acquiring and using governmental or official power. A politician is one professionally engaged in acquiring and using such power. By that standard I have spent most of the years since I left law school as a politician. In speaking of politics, I restrict myself to the political life with which I am most familiar — American politics at the Federal level.

Thus defined, the most painful and troubling condition of political life is the swift growth in importance of governmental power coupled with the steady diminution of the significance of the individual, inexorably transforming him from a wielder to an object of power.

The Presidency

The growth of governmental power, in size and significance, is so self-evident that it needs no support. Only thirty-five years ago Mencken could write: "The rewards of the Presidency are mostly trashy . . . The President continues, of course, to be an eminent man, but only in the sense that Jack Dempsey, Lindbergh, Babe Ruth and Henry Ford have been eminent men." Mencken describes a Presidential day: "All day long the right hon. lord of us all sits listening to bores and quacks. Anon a Secretary rushes in with the news that some eminent movie actor . . . has died, and the President must seize a pen and write a telegram of condolence to the widow. Once a year he is repaid by receiving a cable on his birthday from King George . . . it takes four days hard work to concoct a speech without a sensible word in it. Next day a dam must be opened somewhere. Four Senators get drunk and try to neck a lady politician . . . The Presidential automobile runs over a dog. It rains."

We still mock our Presidents, sometimes brutally, but no longer because they are futile and insignificant. We satirize more out of fear than condescension. The Federal government spends about one seventh of our national wealth and creates more of it. Today a third of the entire labor force works for someone other than a private employer. Science research and technological development are increasingly fueled by public funds. It is the government, not private business, that is held responsible for the condition of the economy: credited with prosperity, blamed for recession and inflation, expected to make the country grow and prosper, to end unemployment and to keep prices down. Of course Washington's power is not equal to such expectations, but it is inconceivable that any President should greet economic dissatisfaction by saying, "There is nothing I can do," or, even worse, "It is none of my business." The first to assault such a forfeiture would be the conservative members of the business establishment. Government today is also charged with the pursuit of justice, and those who are denied their fair expectations by our society look to Washington for help in righting felt wrongs. Social ills, from benighted cities to blighted air, are regarded as the responsibility of government; and Washington is expected to lead the way out of the automobile-choked tunnels in which we are incarcerating ourselves. This most recent election has highlighted another responsibility for government: keeper of the status quo. Many command it to be the protector of all those who are delighted with their new affluence — suburban houses and television sets — and who regard any social turbulence as a threat to their personal position. They ask that government change everything that bothers them, but halt any rising storms which might stain their seeming comfort. This responsibility, which we might call Reaganism, often conflicts with the aims of justice or the modification of our society in the direction of enlarged individual existence. The gap can only be bridged by using the pulpit of high office to convince citizens that the salvation of the oppressed does not endanger the well-being of the many or, where the conflict is a real one, by pursuing justice as the higher good. Unfortunately we have, thus far, attempted to extricate ourselves from this clash of aims by a kind of tokenism; pretending to make war on poverty or enforce civil rights while confining the resources and power to a level totally inadequate for the purpose, thus easing conscience while making sacrifice unnecessary; all of this often colored by a spurious rhetorical even-handedness which equates the violence of a few frustrated Negroes with the huge oppression of millions. Beyond this is the conduct of foreign policy which gives a few men the authority to commit our country to action in all parts of the world, send hundreds of thousands of men to fight wars in unknown lands,

89

and involve the resources and honor of the nation in adventures, promises, programs and acts in every continent. These huge decisions culminate in the now humbly familiar power to decree our destruction, a power less real because it is beyond the comprehension of consciousness but present and infusing all the other acts of government with majesty and terror.

This leap of power is often seen as an increase in the power of the Presidency, both because the President's power has increased disproportionately and because he is more visible to observation. However, the rest of government has shared in growth. The Supreme Court led the social revolution of the Negro. Congress exercises the power with him in denying redress. Congressional authority is often spoken of as a negative power; but this is because we are trapped in that liberal rhetoric which confines positive action to increased spending, greater regulation or new programs. By avoiding this semantic trap we can see that the judgments of Congress are positive ones, even if sometimes unconsciously so: to direct more of our resources toward private consumption than public needs, to calm the fears of the homeowner against black invasion, to deny assistance to developing countries, to support isolationism and chauvinism. These are affirmative and consequential decisions. Only because the modern Presidency tends to move in a more liberal direction can we call Congressional opposition negative. It could well be argued that Congress affirmatively sets the limitations and framework for Presidential action. It not only acts on its own, but it decisively restricts what a President will even dare to propose.

The Federal Government and Foreign Affairs

If the facts of increasing political power are real, the motive force behind that increase is less clear. In foreign affairs only the central government can lead. No conservative disputes that. Thus as America became a world power — in fact, the only global power — the importance of government was bound to increase.

Federal supremacy in foreign affairs inevitably shapes our attitude toward government in every area of its activity. It is part of the naiveté of the conservative position to believe that it is possible to compartmentalize the conduct of public affairs, granting enormous power in the world arena while withdrawing it from domestic concerns. In some measure this increasing power has been produced by the converging flow of historical and psychological processes. The revolution of the New Deal created large new authority for government along with vastly increased expectations by its citizens. Once this process had begun it became difficult to reverse it, because the natural inertia of the American system sweeps it forward in the absence of truly revolutionary opposition. The single conservative administration since Roosevelt could only consolidate and not reverse the flow. Thus expectations and power ride side by side. Added to this is the natural tendency of men in power to seek additions to authority, avoid any renunciation or relinquishment, relish the anguish of decision, and to resent any effort to oppose their will. This interlocked psychological and historical process has been strengthened by our increasing capacity to control events from the center.

Economics and, to a lesser extent, other social sciences have enabled us to achieve a mastery of the operations of society which was not possible before. Mass communication and swift transportation has enabled government to bring its authority and assistance to bear all over the country in a detailed and specific manner, allowing it to construct the rapidly responsive bureaucracy hitherto thought impossible for a nation of continental dimension. Computerization of government, the next stage, will increase the possibilities for central direction. Our widening democratization, partly a result of superior techniques of political organization, has given disadvantaged groups a political power larger than their economic and social power, requiring politicians to respond to their claims. We are past the time of the 1920's when millions of farmers could languish in depression while causing scarcely a ripple in far off Washington. The increasing helplessness of the individual, cut off from traditional ties of family and community, drive him toward a central authority which can help cope with forces, threats and circumstances he feels are beyond his powers. Since grievances and hopes alike can no longer be aired or exercised effectively within smaller units, there is no choice but Washington; and again expectations become the parent of authority. This same dissolution compels the individual to seek new ways to participate in some larger enterprise, leading him to aggrandize the national authority which is both a source of his hopes and frustrations.

The growing rigidity of our social order also closes off traditional alternative outlets of desired change. The closing of the West was the first step. The elimination of unskilled labor, a door through which many entered American society, may prove just as significant. The power of large corporations, the sanctity of the drive for profit, and the exaltation of economic growth are virtually beyond serious challenge; and, in fact, even the most daring political figure restricts himself to minor modifications. In other words, we accept much of our system as fixed, the ideological debate as closed, all of which gives greater strength to the one authority which seems able to channel our institutions — through coercion and guidance — toward desired goals. Private citizens and individual communities often feel helpless in the face of abuses caused by institutions and a philosophy which seems unchallengeable. Thus the air is poisoned in the name of industrialization. Our suburbs become horrors of ugliness, discomfort, and spiritual destruction because the right to buy land and build on it as you please is sacred. The blurred advance of technology makes it impossible for any but the most sophisticated and endowed to weigh the advantage of change against the social ills it may bring. Individuals are forced to turn to the ally which appears strong enough to cope with such overwhelming forces: the central government.

The growth in population and the fantastic mobility of that population has also weakened faith in the ability of social institutions, redirecting hope toward the center. It is, in fact, now a myth that people feel closer to their local government than to the nation. In earlier times, geography, communications and social structure conspired to make local government the center of concern. Now awareness of events and personalities in Washington is ordinarily far more vivid than the circumstances of local affairs. There is more intimate identity with the President and even Congress than with mayors or governors, as any examination of voting statistics, polls, or publications will prove. Despite these growing links, local authority often has a familiarity which better equips it to resolve many difficulties whose variety resist concentrated solutions. Rising wealth also contributes to rising central power.

Although affluence encourages conservatism, modern conservatives are usually more concerned with the content of authority rather than the exercise of power. Thus it is possible to oppose welfare programs on the grounds of big government (as well as a preference for abstraction over compassion), while supporting larger police forces and a range of new coercive powers for the state. (In addition many modern conservatives are on the side of a greatly more interventionist and aggressive foreign policy which would inevitably lead to more formidable and sweeping powers for the central government; the theory being, I suppose, that it is more important to fight radicals abroad than liberals at home.) The motive behind this paradoxical conservative contribution to our general evolution is the desire for protection of the affluent against unpleasant, troubling and threatening social forces.

The State and the Individual

Increasing power for the state is coupled with diminishing significance for the individual. The individual's confidence in his consequence rests on each man's share of mastery over his life and environment. An internal ability to come to terms with the world, to seek a place in the drama, is imperative. But even the most intense and controlled awareness of self will not provide significance to the individual who is constantly denied, rejected and ignored by his world unless he possesses those rare inner resources which allow him to create his own. But that is not politics. (Naturally the two sources are mutual.) As political affairs become more centralized and as personal group and local responsibilities are absorbed, the individual sense of mastery is eroded. For, in fact, his ability to control circumstances is less.

This is not simply a political phenomenon. It saturates our philosophical, technological and social environment. I am not a philosopher, or even a social critic, but the dwindling consequences of the individual in politics cannot be understood apart from the general conditions of society. A politician, unlike occasional artists, cannot stand in brilliant isolation from the commanding values of his time. The successful pursuit of his discipline must reflect the contemporary condition; especially when confined by democratic protections against the willful coercions of a single leader pursuing a personal vision. There is a great deal of room for leadership, but toward places within our sight and comprehension rather than blindly beyond a distant horizon. Thus to seek out the decline of the political individual we must glance at the conditions of the time.

More as metaphor than as precise historical description let me affirm that we are bringing to an end the six hundred year period of the Renaissance. The Renaissance, Michelet explained, was characterized by "man's discovery of the world and of man." Before this, Burckhardt says, man had seen himself as a part of a series of catagories such as his people, party, family, etc. Now, "man became a spiritual individual." As the focus thus shifted there was an effort to see man whole and to describe the essence of being man, a search for a synthesis between man and his world, and an effort to formulate embracing values to guide and ennoble human life. There was a belief in wholeness and a growing faith that incomplete understanding resulted from an imperfect knowledge which we could labor to complete. One of the last glories of the Renaissance and one of its destroyers, Albert Einstein, when faced with theories that assumed the essential role of chance in describing the existence of basic units of the material world asked, "Do you really think God resorts to dice playing?" He spoke in the tradition of a science which encouraged the belief that the free play of inquiring mind would lead us to a harmonious and complete description of reality. Philosophers and artists alike struggled to grasp man's nature as incorporated into statements of faith, and true representations of reality.

Now this search for unity is dissolving. We live, instead, in a time of fragmentation and dissection in search of the components of the sensible world. Religion has little impact on our ordinary behavior and therefore our lives. The concept of God as the source of moral command dissolves into mystical generalizations or disappears. Belief lingers but rarely lives. Efforts at systematic philosophy are scorned, ignored or become the province of esoteric technicians. St. Augustine and Spinoza become Norman O. Brown and Marshall McLuhan. Art continues the process of fragmentation, reducing objects to light and form, regarding the elements as ultimate description rather than parts of a larger construction. We dissect emotions and actions alike to create confused sadness and absurdity. The pervasive hunger is more for experience than for meaning. The insistent quest for the nature and meaning of man begins to yield, as psychology and biochemistry break us up into instinct, drives, creations of other beings, molecules, chemical codes and electrical patterns; until the question itself begins to lose meaning in its historic sense. Man is becoming a physical phenomenon, different from other life only in degree, all his complexities ultimately describable and predictable. The truth lies in the pieces of the puzzle and not the picture they make. For that picture is largely the random, purposeless assembly of myriad components in a single unit of living flesh.

I do not mean to condemn this process, merely to describe it. Nor can anyone preclude the chance it may lead to a new kind of understanding and integrity. Yet it adds up to a profound difference in our view of ourselves. This drive to reduce man and his world to its elements is of enormous power. For it seems to give control, much as the man who owns the bricks can dictate the shape of the house. It is a quest with the force of primitive religion. No one denies that fragmentation must go on, and that new science and technology are to be pursued regardless of the values they imperil. They are the values. It was possible at one time to ask what difference it made if the earth revolved around the sun if knowing this might deprive us of God. But Galileo is our hero, not his foes; while the drive for this type of understanding has a momentum of its own which is highly neurotic and unstopable.

Is the Individual Free?

I see this only as a central current, mixed with many historic pursuits. The philosophy of existentialism, for example, tries to reconcile much of modern life with the glory of the individual. It too, however, must assume that the individual exists and is free, beliefs which are in profound question.

Our American culture, more intensely than any other, reflects this fragmentation. A man as eminent and perceptive as André Malraux charges that the United States, for all its great achievements, lacks a national culture. He can say this if he looks for culture in its classical sense — a structure of value and meaning embodying itself in certain forms. Our culture is different than that. It is rooted in our whole history as a nation. It is a culture of restlessness. Its principal values are change and movement feeding the hunger for experience. This culture is now sweeping the world, not only as painting and theater, but in the beat of our music and the exaltation of technology. It is a culture eminently suited to the process of fragmentation, to dissolution and uncertainty. For it does not demand the resting place that unity and wholeness provide. It transforms values into psychology, drives, hungers and actions. It denies ideology, replacing belief with conviction.

All of this threatens our spiritual existence, but there is also a more hopeful prospect that we may ultimately arrive at a firm base for the companionship of man; a base made up of the internal realities of the desire for protection and dignity and the ability to recognize and feel the similar desires of our fellows.

I do not decry the culture or the process. We cannot ask people to believe that which is no longer self-evident and which is denied by the evidence of the senses. The important thing is to come to terms with an age whose ultimate expression could be the destruction of the human race or which may offer us a humanism more enduringly founded on psychological reality rather than on abstraction, ideology, or classical religion.

If we are lost or alien or driven, within this society, it is in large measure because fragmentation conflicts with the need for mastery. Human identity requires mastery: both self-mastery and some shaping share in the concentric world around us, a place in the company of other men. How difficult it has become to find this in the midst of dissolution and constant movement. Yet those who are deprived of mastery for themselves are often driven to yield it to others, ultimately forfeiting their freedom. I offer these ideas with understandable uncertainty. At least as metaphor they may help us understand what is happening in our political life.

Since political and social institutions are conservative they lag behind thought and art. Yet here too a process of fragmentation is in full tide, a reflection of more profound currents. Many of the structures which gave importance and security to the individual are dissolving. Family ties stretch and break as the gap between the generations widens, and as more spacious possibilities of mobility — occupational and geographical — make it easier to indulge natural hostilities. The community disappears, as comprehensible units of society blend into the huge, sprawling, accidental monstrosities of our cities. Science describes our world, and life itself, in terms beyond ordinary understanding. Cities and technology, production and population grow, spreading and change powered by forces which seem beyond the control, and even the desire, of individual man. A handful of men in remote capitols shape the course of our nation in the world and hold existence hostage to their wisdom or impulse or sanity. Smaller groups where we could once belong and be needed, because we could encompass them with the mind's eye, are disappearing. Many of the activities we once thought to control, e.g., "What shall our town be like?," seem beyond that control.

All of this, thrusting the individual away from influence and understanding, feeds restlessness. Thus alienation, rage, desperation and a growing sense of futility increasingly scar our political life. Two forms of reaction emerge. Violence, protest, and new extreme ideologies reflect the urgent desire of many of the vital to assert their importance and to matter in the enterprise of society. While among the larger numbers who lack overflowing vitality is a growing desire to protect and conserve, a fear of change, and the determination to hold fast to what they have because they are losing confidence in their own ability to shape the future.

These are among the principal phenomena of modern political life. We see it in manifold, sometimes frightening forms: unreasoning conservatism and violence, the New Right and the New Left, Minutemen, and John Birchers, Black Muslims, and Southern secessionists, the search for a hero and the need for an enemy. A close analysis would show differences and even some continuities with our traditions. Essentially, these are forms which only appear to be contradictory, for they all help provide an inner sense of importance in some larger service. Thus a growing sense of impotence is charged with danger. It can polarize groups and individuals creating a nation of strangers, not only creating extremism but an unwillingness to face problems or to act until difficulties have virtually overwhelmed us. It can also mean the loss of the greatest opportunity ever given to an entire nation: to lead the entire world in the path of compassion and justice. For we are the first country in the modern world to combine unparalleled wealth and power with a set of beliefs which charts such a course rather than self-aggrandizement. All of this will be lost unless individual citizens can find the faith in themselves which is the source of national direction and generosity of deed.

The Role of Practical Politics

The machine may already be out of control, but my profession compels me to be an optimist. Far-reaching structural and ideological shifts may be needed, but I see no present possibility for revolution nor would I know where to lead one. As a politician I can only offer political approaches, moving as fast as possible within the framework of our institutions and values. There may be more brilliant and daring ways to kill a bull than with the cape and sword, but not for the man in the ring. Perhaps ultimately the sum of such modification will create a new form.

I must now descend, therefore, from the satisfying heights of abstraction and unprovable observation to the stadium of practical politics. Still, action must take direction from thought and general purpose if it is to be more than greed. The human problems created by fragmentation are far more than political. Yet they are political also. The isolation and lessening significance of the individual with its consequent human degradation and social dangers can be confronted on the political front with new policies and structures of government designed to give each man the capacities and opportunity to find a moving role in the life of his society.

To understand this is a matter of architecture, but doing it is for builders. It is the building I would now like to discuss.

Part of the approach is in the specific content of our policies: shifting resources from individual consumption to social ills and a modification of the values which tend to regard all changes wrought by technology or the pursuit of business expansion paramount to all other aims. "You can't stand in the way of progress," is a favorite American expression, concealing a definition of progress which rests on very special traditions and beliefs.

Decentralization of Government Action

This is a subject of such spacious dimension that I hope to develop it another day. I am concerned with the deeply related and dependent problem of the way we should conduct these poli-

98

cies; the political structures which can both meet the specific ills and meet them so as to drastically enlarge the sense and reality of individual relevance and participation. What structural changes can combat the consequences of social fragmentation by giving individuals a sense of direct, intimate and personal mastery over the conditions of their own life and share in the larger enterprises and adventures of society? The most hopeful path, I believe, is the decentralization of government action: helping states, communities and private groups assume increasing responsibilities for the activities conducted by government. It is to shift the political programs which flow from idealism and need toward those units of action which are small enough and close enough for a more intimate human relationship, while at the same time widening the outlets for direct personal participation.

This is a suggestion which is far removed from the old argument against collective action. It assumes that problems must be solved collectively and, in large measure, through units of government. The issue is one of structure and organization, flowing from painful assumptions about the condition of political man in America. In fact, even modern conservatism is coming closer to this view. During his campaign for mayor Mr. Buckley argued for city action against a host of problems from pollution to a scarcity of bicycle paths. He assaulted Federal action in the same fields because it was "none of their business," making his opposition more geographical than ideological.

Although decentralization is designed to help combat the social and spiritual ills of fragmentation, it also coincides with the fact that centralized bureaucracies tend to become increasingly ineffective and coercive in direct proportion to the scope and intricacy of the problem they are established to solve.

We are sometimes told that recruiting more able people is the answer to bureaucratic inadequacy. People of high abilities are necessary, but much of the inadequacy is inherent in the effort to deal with enormously complex problems from the center. This was less apparent when much of government action consisted of grants, subsidies or insurance for individuals. It is not difficult to write checks. Now, however, we find it necessary to apply technical skills to our cities and educational programs, to techniques of combating pollution and methods of overcoming poverty. One need only look at the fantastic labyrinth of welfare programs, the monstrous incapacities of the Department of Health, Education, and Welfare — operated by one of the best teams of executives in government — as well as the foreseeable futilities of the new Departments of Housing and Urban Development and Transportation, to realize something is wrong with the approach. Even the Russians, in their far more ambitious effort to manage an entire economy from Moscow buildings, are reluctantly reaching the same kind of conclusion and turning to decentralization of activity.

Moreover, decentralization may well lose new energy and purpose in pursuit of a more just, liberating and satisfying society. By directly engaging individuals, and giving them a sense of participation and commitment, we can increase the desire for goals toward which many remain indifferent or even hostile while they are the province of a removed and abstract central government. For example, if we could involve large numbers of Americans in programs of help to underdeveloped countries — and I will suggest ways to do this — they would become increasingly convinced, and even passionate, about the moral and political necessity for such programs.

Decentralization will not only shift responsibility to state and local government. Private groups can be directly involved, as they are in the community action program of the war against poverty. Yet local government would be the principal reliance. One of the objections to such a course is the incapacity of local government as well as its occasional corruption. It is unfair, however, to test the ability of local officials against an ideal of good government. It must be matched with the abilities of Federal agencies where inefficiency is not unknown. Moreover, responsibility breeds ability and decentralization gives responsibility. Hours are spent in town councils arguing about the placement of new traffic lights, while the great issues are debated in Washington. It is little wonder that men of vitality and ability are reluctant to serve or lose enthusiasm. Even so, the importance of political life is already attracting more able men into local public service; and the ability to solve problems is becoming a requirement of election to state houses and city halls. Moreover, decentralization is not abdication. It is possible, as I will outline, to set standards for local action and by enforcing these standards to raise the level of performance.

Once you accept the desirability of decentralization there are many practical and resistant difficulties. Different problems will command different structures, requiring political creativity and experiment. But there are some common obstacles and methods of approach.

In a moment I will discuss some specific examples, but the guiding principle should be of national standards, of varying degree of specificity, while transferring to local government or private groups the needed resources, and the responsibility for decision, action and policy making within those standards. We are doing this to some degree in programs ranging from the war against poverty to the construction of waste treatment plants on our rivers. Moreover, standards may be educational rather than coercive. A small but fascinating model is the President's Committee on Physical Fitness. That Committee drew up model programs of physical training for schools, community organization and individuals. Though it had no regulatory power and hardly any money the result has been a flourishing of physical fitness programs across the country. The same technique might well be applied to the formulation of model school curricula, child care centers, traffic control programs, and in many other activities. Many of the deficiencies in the conduct of society flow from the fact that citizens are unaware of the dimensions of a problem and of the possibilities for solution. Nor can they command the technical and intellectual resources which are increasingly necessary to devise effective programs. However, many standards will go beyond counsel and information and impose physical and policy requirements. It will always be desirable, however, to keep standards as loose as possible consistent with effective direction.

The Heller Plan

The fact that local government lacks the resources — financial and human — to cope with even its present difficulties is a powerful barrier to decentralization. Walter Heller has proposed that the Federal government simply turn over, presumably on a per capita basis, some of its revenue to the states. I am a great admirer of Mr. Heller and respect the liberal impulse behind his idea. It is, however, essentially a counsel of defeat. It does not increase the resources available for social problems and may even lessen them, depending on what the states do with the money. It assumes that Congress will react to rising revenue by cutting taxes rather than by helping the poor or rebuilding our cities, and it hopes to forestall this by transferring revenue out of congressional hands and out of the national budget; an objective which some conservatives have not fully understood. Thus the Heller Plan assumes that the politics of inertia — where programs are neither eliminated nor substantially increased — will dominate the Federal structure. It also subsumes the praiseworthy faith that state governments will use this money for critical public needs. Some will use it well and some will not. I expect that increasing local ability and public purpose will flow from the mounting responsibilities which come with decentralization. This does not mean, however, that the necessary ability and integrity are already sitting in every state house crippled only by lack of money. It is a notorious fact that many state legislatures are more responsive to private interests, from loan companies to home builders, than is the Congress. It is quite possible, under the Heller Plan, that New York residents may end up paying Federal taxes to reduce the tax burden on property owners in Indiana — to take a purely hypothetical case. Moreover, some assurance is needed that revenue collected across the nation is not sent to areas where its benefits are denied to Negroes.

Many of these problems can be avoided, and state competence raised, by turning resources over to the states for concrete purposes of varying generality and with specific standards of performance, rather than by lump sum payments. In addition we may find it is not the state but the city or smaller communities and private groups which are the appropriate unit of action. Decentralization should go farther and deeper than the state house. Still, the Heller Plan would be worth trying if there were no alternative. However, there are many alternatives. They vary in the extent to which they restrict and direct state and local use of nationally collected resources. They provide a great deal more flexibility and strengthened assurance that critical needs will be met. Since I am not an economist I only speak in general terms about matters which are highly technical in detail.

First, is to establish Federal standards and guidelines in specific areas, e.g., housing and pollution control, coupled with the allocation of Federal funds to the local units which meet the requirements. This is the structure of the anti-pollution program for rivers and the new Demonstration Cities Act.

Second, is the possibility of a series of credits against Federal income taxes for additional state taxes earmarked for specific purposes, e.g., education. There would have to be some safeguards against the transfer of state revenues to other purposes in order to reduce local taxes; and possibly the establishment of a rising base line which would take growing state population and wealth into consideration.

Third, is a variant of the Heller Plan: general appropriations to local authorities for a variety of specified purposes, e.g., health, education, housing, training, etc., allowing the state or locality to set its own priorities. Tax credits can be used in the same way.

I am sure there are other fiscal devices, e.g., allowing states to require tolls on the interstate highway system if they are devoted to certain public purposes. They all have in common the desire to increase the resources available to states as an instrument of decentralization.

Recruitment and Training of Personnel

Money and programs are useless without competent people to administer them. Human skill is harder to find than cash, both because able men are often not attracted to local government and because we lack trained people. Sometimes imaginative political leadership will recruit men of unusual ability, as Richard Lee has proven in New Haven. As greater responsibility flows outward from Washington, and as the work of states and communities becomes more important, public life will be increasingly attractive. Still we have been slipshod and neglectful in training men for public service, even at the Federal level; a defect which is more serious as problems become more technical.

Decentralization demands a generous effort to train and encourage people toward public service. Again the possible techniques are numerous. Let me mention a few possibilities: Federal grants to universities to establish training programs, perhaps even a foundation similar to the National Science Foundation; Federally financed training institutes for young men or established civil servants, either as national institutions or under the control of regions or states; subsidies for the salaries and expenses of highly skilled people; model codes for government workers embracing incentive, evaluating tenure, recognition, etc. These codes would simply be optional guidelines for local government. Perhaps a Governor's Conference could set such a project in motion.

Many similar things are already done in other fields. For example, Federal effort — seed money as well as full support — has enormously increased the number and quality of men and women engaged in scientific research. Certainly public service is no less important. Of course, even this effort will not coerce able men into public service; although it may help increase their numbers and ability. However, the Peace Corps and poverty program, the civil rights movement and my own observations across the country, strengthen my conviction that large numbers of our citizens are seeking some effective way to serve society, and they are often willing to give up the attractions of private life for such an opportunity. In fact, that conviction underlies some of the philosophical premises of this paper. If we do not provide this chance, our most valuable national resource will be dissipated. Ultimately an able public service rests on aggressive and imaginative political leadership at every level. It may be coming. There is a growing public demand for candidates of ability, more able men are lured by politics and, as the old political structures crumble, a growing number of men are elected because they offer more promise of being able to cure public afflictions.

I do not wish to elaborate on the many concrete areas where decentralization of activity is immediately practical. These will be limited only by the extent of our political and technical inventiveness. We already have several experiments to point the way. Still it would be unfair to give only a few specific examples of realistic applications of the general principle. I will sketch these examples in a general way. Carrying them out will require rigorous and detailed examination. The Peace Corps was a few sentences in a campaign speech. The law it required takes up many pages. So it is with nearly all ideas destined for government action. I have discussed a few of these proposals in previous public speeches. A few are incarcerated in White House memoranda which languish in files awaiting the casual curiosity of historians. Some have even glimpsed the light of political day in the pronouncements of high officials and in legislative proposals.

An Example: Foreign Policy

Let me begin with the most difficult area of all: foreign policy. It is desirable and possible, and it may be essential, to turn over a substantial part of the foreign assistance program to state administration. Let me give an example of what I mean. The single most important economic problem for the developing countries is agriculture. The large majority of their populations work the soil. Agricultural development is essential for food, to lessen dependence on foreign imports and thus conserving foreign exchange, and to provide a market for industry by raising the income for farmers. The United States has an enormously successful agricultural economy; and the skill, know-how and energy which built that economy can be found in the states rather than in Washington. The men, knowledge and experience are to be found in the great agricultural universities, state departments of agriculture and among private associations of farmers and growers. I have proposed that we ask a particular state government to administer our agricultural development program in a specified country or countries, giving the state all Federal money set aside for this purpose. Would the state respond? I had an opportunity to test that before I left the government. I discussed this idea with President Kennedy, not too many months before his death. He was enthusiastic, wanted to go ahead, and even wrote two or three personal memoranda to the State Department urging action. The consequent inaction was a dramatically illuminating example of the ability of a bureaucracy to frustrate a President. Still they did not dare ignore him entirely. The first project (which was to be "experimental" even though the President had already decided the general policy) was to ask the state of California to run the agricultural program in Chile.

California has great technical resources. It has many of the same problems and crops, similar variations in climate, and even looks like a very fat version of Chile. Its population is larger with approximately the same acreage of arable land, and it still man-

105

ages to export 80-90 percent of its production while Chile imports food. I was a member of the team which went to Sacramento to discuss the project with Governor Brown. He was enthusiastic and nearly all the concerned officials of his government shared his enthusiasm. They devoted many hours to planning and discussion, promised to devote substantial energy to the program, and to hire additional people. All of this culminated with the signing of a general agreement in the White House by the President and the Governor.

For many reasons the project has not worked as I hoped, and as I think President Kennedy hoped, primarily because AID was unwilling to let go of responsibility and decision for a large part of its program. Yet it is just this kind of delegation which is essential to any state-wide feeling of significant participation. The meager fruits of this hopeful and spacious idea is something now called Partners for Progress in which state agencies, universities, private groups — in California and elsewhere — are asked to run specific projects. Yet the entire politico-dramatic impact depended upon our willingness to say to the state, "This is your job, let's see what California can do." The arguments for such an approach are, in my view, overwhelming: The states are better at agriculture than AID can ever hope to be and would do a better job. Although states would spend Federal money, the drama, publicity, and leadership from the State House, would inevitably summon widespread contributions of money and talent from the private sector and local government. Growers' groups might offer technical assistance, while high schools provided scholarships and established exchange programs. Communities would "adopt" counterpart communities in the developing country. The possibilities are endless; and enough of this began to happen to prove they were realistic.

Such a program would give thousands of individuals and many organizations the chance to participate in one of the most important overseas ventures of the American nation. In the process we could help create a widespread political constituency for foreign aid. No longer would such help be a remote endeavor in which a few anonymous bureaucrats in Washington hand over large chunks of taxpayers' money to equally remote people in some unknown capitol. There is little doubt of the basic compassion of Americans toward other countries or of their interest in the people of foreign lands. Any foreign visitor who lives here for a while can testify to that. But the current program does not touch these basic emotions because it is abstract and removed. As a result, the foreign aid program, morally imperative and vital to our interest, is doomed. It was that sense of impending doom which helped explain President Kennedy's interest. The intervening years have seen a steady erosion of a most generous and necessary concept.

Another Example: American Cities

Another area for decentralization, and one closer to home, is the American city. Having worked in this area while in the White House, I know that the problem of the cities is enormously complex. It is not one problem but a hundred: urban renewal and rehabilitation of rundown structures, new financing technique and private development corporations, control of land speculation and new suburban slums, breaking up ghettos and giving people a place to play, efficient transportation and mastery of the automobile. We may need to rebuild entire central cities or construct huge new satellite metropolises. The condition and future prospect of our cities is the greatest single threat to the quality of American life. Many who live in major urban areas are already the victims of conditions which confine, stifle and degrade their daily life to an extent unthinkable half a century ago. Nor is this a problem for the poor alone. They are the chief victims, but all must breathe the air, fight the traffic, do without nature and fear violence.

Instead of attacking problem after problem we must begin by asking what kind of a city we want to live in, and what kind of a city we want for our children. As we approach the problem on this spacious scale certain central realities emerge: The cities do not have the money to meet their problems. Uncontrolled growth and change must be replaced by long-range planning which encompasses the entire urban area across municipal and state lines.

I believe we should adopt a Marshall Plan approach for the American cities. Resources on a large scale would be made available to those urban areas which prepared a comprehensive program for future development; including problems from land use to housing codes and water systems. The Federal government could give technical assistance in planning, set certain standards,

107

and ensure that the program was being carried forward. The basic responsibility for decision and action would rest with the city and its people. This would not only help meet the more general imperatives of decentralization, but would provide a powerful incentive for the cooperation across historic political jurisdictions which is the condition of effective action.

There are many other specific areas where decentralization is possible. Anti-poverty and job retraining programs should be increasingly handed over to community groups not, as is now the case, drawn closer and closer to the Federal government. Aid to education might well be administered to a far larger degree by local boards of education, subject only to the most general standards. Instead of threatening to draft all young Americans for public service we could encourage and finance a host of varied volunteer groups to perform public services at state and community levels in order to provide an outlet for those many Americans still anxious to find an answer to the question "what can you do for your country." Many Federal installations and services could well be subject to greater local supervision. For example, we might establish local Boards of Directors for post offices, permitting the communities to decide, within the limits of available resources, the kind of postal service they require, even hire and fire postmasters and, at least, to air their complaints.

Much of this will appear sloppy and chaotic. Some of it will certainly be confused. It is always easier to yearn for the illusory neatness of central direction and control, and assume it is more effective. That is an assumption which is often wrong, and which must now be questioned across the board of Federal activity; even if we add to the confusion, that is certainly acceptable in order to meet the profound necessities and values involved in decentralization. It may even turn out to be creative. In fact, I cannot remember a single, unconfused government organization that produced an important new idea.

I do not assume that proposals such as these will remedy what Norman Mailer calls "the plague" of modern life or halt the flow toward fragmentation and futility. Certainly the content of our actions is equally important, fused with its shape. Politics, too, is only part of the story. The march of values, ideas, change and instinct may be too resistless, and too deeply embedded in our modern condition to yield, even slightly, to leadership and political invention. Perhaps the changes required are far more convulsive and profound than most of us can formulate. As a practicing politician I can only hope and speak of those things which seem to reach toward the limits of foreseeable possibility. For any more than this a prophet is needed.

There is no return to past forms of community and family strength, or the comforting systems of belief which gave every man his place and guide. There is only the certainty that a new order of things is taking shape and, as men whose life is action, we say, as Stephen Vincent Benét said of the age he saw approaching:

> prophets, old or young,
> Bawl out their strange despair
> Or fall in worship there,
>
> . . .
>
> Say neither, in their way,
> "It is a deadly magic and accursed,"
> Nor "It is blest," but only "It is here."

If the time is filled with terrors, still the meaning of what is and what is to be is veiled from us. There is much of magnificence and glory in what we have done, and many liberating blessings have been added to human life. If history is "inscrutable," its mystery can conceal hope as well as danger. Certainly we act on the belief that we can bend events towards human good, even while we are aware of the dim uncertainties of that which we are laboring to create. No man or nation or leader of nations can truly foresee the result of momentous and expectant ventures. At times it is tragedy. At times it ennobles humanity, just as the patrons of Florence could not know they were spurring a revolution in human thought, or our own early leaders that they were establishing structures which would influence the growth of liberty in a world of monarchs and despots. The specific ideas of this paper have no such pretensions. They are a contribution to the changes of purpose and direction needed within this country, while beyond lies a world role whose possibilities and obligations we have dimly begun to grasp. Perhaps, through politics — the collective actions of a people — we can help direct the torrent of change toward a world society which will restore and amplify the confidence of individual man in his role in the drama of existence; and build on that confidence until we have the strength, for the first time, to encompass all humanity in the play. I do not know, but there is one sign. For a brief moment President John Kennedy illuminated the possibility that the resistant frontiers of nation, race and culture might be submerged in common purpose. It was not that the people of many nations admired him and saw him as a center of their own hopes. It was that he made them feel more confident of their own powers, and revealed some fragile but unexpected sense of common humanity. He was a very rare man, but he proved that there were marvelous possibilities. Someone said that it is the task of a genius to set a course which more ordinary men can take up when he is gone. That is what we can try to do.

CHAPTER 8

The Conference in Review— Reports of the Discussion Groups

RAPPORTEUR No. 1
Harry Woolf, Ph.D.
Chairman, Department of the History of Science
The Johns Hopkins University

At the beginning of Shakespeare's play, *Henry V*, there is a prologue in which the spokesman for what is to come apologizes to the audience for having to cram the events of so many years into an hourglass. I advance the same plea on behalf of our modest discourse, though the years are reduced to hours and the hourglass to the sweep of a minute hand.

I am somewhat uncertain as to the proper role of a rapporteur. So I am taking the easiest of several possible courses by summarizing simply and sequentially the points of view advanced in our group — primarily those accepted, and perhaps a word or two on those which were rejected.

The first discussion centered on the statement by Dean Walton. Two salient points struck our attention as emerging strongly from his presentation. They are the obvious role of the corporate manager as the representative of the stockholders, securely established by accepted practice and tradition, and the nascent and as yet ill-defined definition of his position as a trustee of and for the general public he serves beyond the lines of corporate ownership. This dual role defines no clear zones of action. It represents an area open to imaginative managerial leadership where proven skills may be employed in the creation of programs for social and economic action.

Our group was also concerned with the image of the manager as he appears to those with other kinds of power in society, or

111

perhaps to those who seem to have the promise of power. In the latter case we had in mind, for example, the college student and others in the academic world who are playing a larger role in the disposition of national funds and decisions about national policy.

Dean Walton's comments also precipitated a discussion of the "untouchables" in the caste order of the American economy. How does one identify them and get at them? What can the manager of large corporate enterprises do about the underdeveloped aspects of the domestic economy? Underprivilege and deprivation occur at various levels in the lower reaches of the economic order. Can the course of action be identical for each of these segments?

All of these issues and more are some of the stresses at work upon the very concept of the manager, warping its structure and altering its character so that assumptions of twenty years or even a decade ago no longer seem valid. I cannot give you answers to the questions which exercised our combined wit and intelligence, for the seminar did not produce answers, though some were given that were novel or extraordinary, but it recognized general problems and did agree that transformations had taken place — reinforcing one of Dean Walton's major points about the larger pattern of change in contemporary society.

There was considerable enthusiasm about the subject of human behavior which came to us from Dr. Delgado's paper. His concern with factual explanations of human behavior and the possibilities that the kind of research he was undertaking would some day lead toward a richer understanding of personality, essentially derived from a sort of mechanical physico-chemical foundation was especially stimulating. Dr. Delgado should not be charged with so limiting man, but this was the area of his professional interest and he was concerned with making some of its extraordinary accomplishments more understandable.

There was much praise for this world of fact rather than theory, or speculation. One of the members of our little seminar raised the question — the fearful question which seems to plague a much larger percentage of the population than is present here — of the danger of a complete scientific layout of the human personality, of a complete determinism. This was raised in other contexts by other spokesmen, with considerable denial of that possibility both by scientists present and by those from other walks of life.

112

One significant question raised in our group under this rubric was the role of insurance companies in contributing to basic research. It came out of the question of understanding personality. I think there was universal agreement that the amount of money spent was not large enough and that perhaps in looking for new frontiers in these matters, insurance companies should be concerned with increased research in the social sciences.

In this same context it was suggested that research ought to be directed towards the examination of questions of security, the individual, the national welfare and interrelationships among these groups of concerns as seen from the social scientist or behavioral point of view. Long-range results, valuable to insurance companies and to society at large, might emerge from such investigations freely pursued.

Following Mr. Heckscher's paper with its central theme that the city should be made for man, there was some specific dissatisfaction with the notion that the ideal city for analysis was New York City. One point selected from others in this discussion was raised by a question: does the insurance industry have a responsibility to insist upon an orderly approach to design in the building of cities, since it has some role in the mortgaging of those buildings which are constructed? Could it insist on esthetic standards? Should it attempt to impose some criteria of this kind on the borrower?

Generally the group felt the insurance business had no official role to play in this sense. Although the point was made that the values which are built into the personalities of the participants in the process of applying for and giving loans, might subconsciously or indirectly help shape of things to come for urban humanity.

There was a chorus of almost universal approval for Dr. Dubos' paper. Especially stimulating was his emphasis on the profound effect of environment, especially the very early environment, on the child, and his detailed and carefully presented analysis of what we may call the ecology of intelligence in the critical first five or six years of a child's life. This was very exciting for most of us, especially when he talked about the impact on potential mental development, the potential for maximizing what an individual may be, that is set so firmly by the experiences of those early years.

This sort of scientific judgment has of course immediate and obvious consequences in programs such as Head Start, which attempt to get at the child before he reaches school. As one member who was a vigorous and colorful participant in the seminar said, "He registered with me!"

With Rabbi Heschel's paper, which emphasized the uniqueness of man, most of us found that he essentially reinforced what we have come to believe in any case. Rabbi Heschel's argument that the divine element in man enables him to stand alone, to be future oriented and to act on the basis of that awareness in the face of adversity found ready support in our group.

Dr. Boulding's talk presented us with a complex of stimulating topics, forcefully delivered and pedagogically profound. We could only wish for more time to elaborate upon even a few of the points he raised. The question of the horizontal development of technology itself (to use his phrase), the exploration of interrelationships between technology and other aspects of life, examined with anthropological eye, offer extraordinary possibilities for analysis of the human condition. Professor Boulding suggested that the flow of history is dominated by the themes of love, loyalty and legitimacy. We fail to realize that once these forces are released, they have an existence of their own in the evolution of the integrative state. Legitimacy and the pathology of its pursuit, for example, powerfully affect the economics of the industrial and technological order of society. With none of these things could we quarrel, nor would we want to, for we felt that his emphasis on the role of non-economic factors affecting national and international economics was very important indeed. Some of us would argue, however, with his historical exploration of the rise of science in the West and its failure to appear in traditional China, but this was not after all one of his central themes. In general, our group was greatly stimulated by Professor Boulding's comments, captured as we were by his capacity to enclose so much, from the concept of a "grants" economy to that of love in the social order, with epigrammatic wit and high style.

Our greatest enthusiasm was reserved for Mr. Goodwin's paper. We agreed to a man with his main thesis about the possibilities of decentralization, especially as it might be applied in unexpected areas, such as foreign aid. This argument was very well advanced though some of us would differ with him on the merit of his oversimplified judgment and encapsulated rendition of the Renaissance.

One learned, from the story of his mission to California to educate the Governor to the possibility of a state program for overseas exchange with Latin America, of the kind of thing that might be done — a mission from high places to educate and direct our leaders for new roles commensurate with the decentralization he spoke about. One of our seminar members added a variant to that theme and suggested we might look in the future to the *have* states making contributions directly to the *have-not* states within the United States, as a kind of spinal-cord bypass of communications to the Federal brain.

We liked his emphasis on the role of problem solvers in the fracturing of old loyalties — problem solvers who get elected to office, of course! We were interested in exploring the problem of how one brings about increased individual participation in local affairs, and we were also interested in the definitions that might be arrived at for various standards set by a Federal government for use and application in regions or in states.

RAPPORTEUR No. 2

James R. Wiggins, Ph.D.

Associate Dean, College of Arts and Sciences

Converse College

I would summarize our group sessions in this way: we struck some sparks; we found considerable mystification, and we experienced a fair amount of discomfort. This proves that we are human. We did, however, develop some definite responses to the papers presented and they shall be reported very briefly for your appraisal.

Since Professor Woolf has commented *in extenso* on the depth and quality of the two contributions made by Dean Walton and Dr. Delgado, I shall begin by emphasizing those portions of my report which relate meaningfully to the analysis of urbanism provided so urbanely by Mr. Heckscher. The initial reaction was to fault the Speaker for his tendency to think that all cities are like New York. There were some non-New Yorkers in our group who felt that if Paris is the heart of France, New York certainly is not the heart of America. Several members of our group suggested that one reason the cities are in trouble is that they are populations

115

representing accurately the varying values of our pluralistic society. There may be tensions generated by the unfortunate tendency of some people to impose their tastes on others.

Since Mr. Heckscher's proposals were specific, concrete and precise they elicited the usual chorus from those who support and from those who reject his formulations. Clearly efforts to revitalize any city, including New York, must involve the cooperative actions of the business community, the industrial community and the political — as we keep saying — power structure. With *total* community involvement, several other cities are moving toward the realization of the goals Mr. Heckscher so clearly identified. If, therefore, total community involvement is crucial and if urban evils are to be reduced it still does not follow that good results are made possible thereby. We cannot forget the long view as we are correcting holes in the pavements. And with the long view the objective is always reached by a series of short steps.

The dissent came from some members who spurned the prescription of a New York or any other metropolis as a series of green belts or parks. Parks, thought some, were fine things in their place. But there was vocal enthusiasm for the hurlyburly, for the excitement and variety of the city, for its unplanned spontaneity, for its mosaic of bricks even more than for its expanse of lawns. The central city is still central! For our nation the spires of the central city, like ancient cathedrals, still inspire and excite us. Few of our group looked with favor on the disappearance of the metropolis even though it is in a present state of decay.

Now may I turn the focus to Dr. Dubos and his brilliant presentation. His analysis of the uniqueness of the individual, the availability of choice, and the responsibility for choices made reinforced and amplified the views of Dr. Delgado. We welcomed the summation: "Man is most human at times of decision — when he is making a choice."

How man makes decisions and the goals for whose achievement such decisions are taken lead directly to the question of the legitimacy of decision-making. And this theme, in turn, moves us directly into the mainstream of concern expressed in Professor Boulding's challenging thesis. Perhaps there was a misreading of the Boulding position in his allusions to the inadequacies of the exchange system as a mechanism for integration and love as an instrument of legitimacy. But it was the consensus of our group that there is a general element of legitimacy in fair exchange, which seemed to be questioned by Professor Boulding. Redistribution of ownership through exchange, entered into freely, has the same attributes of legitimacy assigned to other exchanges, and stands in marked contrast to confiscation of property under threat of violence or through use of violence. We believe that Professor Boulding would accept the likelihood that exchange may benefit both parties, and hence fall within the rules of legitimacy. One other principle of legitimacy was the fragmentation of love and the integration of people.

The creative address of Richard Goodwin this morning was positive and challenging. We were uncertain whether the fragmentation of American society underscored by Mr. Goodwin has gone quite so far as he has suggested. Perhaps the present appearance of fragmentation is essentially a stage in the development of a new synthesis.

By way of both summary and of original contribution from our discussion group, I should report that one of the "anti-fragmentation" patterns of America often surprises visitors from other lands. This is the pervasive determination to do good for other people through *voluntary* gifts of time and money. Even after taxes, Americans by the millions spend their leisure in service to fellow man. Decentralization of Federal programs may be a promising approach, but if it tends to reduce the voluntary man-to-man support found throughout the Nation the price may be too high.

We know the great difference between the mercenary and the personal. The human touch seems to be most human where there is no *quid pro quo* in the direct sense and here Boulding seems most correct. Impersonalized "goodness" for pay cannot compare, in the American tradition, with personalized giving for "nothing." It would be tragic to impinge further on this pattern of life.

I conclude with one personal observation. We have talked much about alienation and I wish to relate it to my own experiences. I live in the Industrial Crescent of the Southeast which is the center of the textile industry. Perhaps this is why I think of alienation as a separation from the *fabric* of human experience. This fabric of human experience has a warp and a woof, a vertical dimension and a horizontal dimension.

We may look on the warp as the *time dimension* of the fabric in which we humans either find a place or do not become fully human. The woof is the *contemporary* strand in which we must also, to be wholly human, find a connection.

Our cities are plagued by two kinds of alienation. First is the alienation of the man who is completely enmeshed in the contemporary, who has no sense of what man's experience has shown or what it projects into the future. The "woofed" human sees every event as unprecedented, and "bends" with it. For our second type, we have the warped man who is out of touch with the contemporary. He may be so preoccupied with the past that he cannot connect himself with the real social world that surrounds him.

To be ripped loose from either dimension of this fabric of human experience stunts the humanity of man. We cannot move smoothly in our individual experience, it seems to me, unless we are — in the city or without — knit into at least these two dimensions of the human spirit.

RAPPORTEUR No. 3

C. Douglas McGee, Ph.D.

Department of Philosophy

Bowdoin College

I will first talk about the two problems which were central to Monday's discussion. The first was — to coin a phrase — "Who is man?" The second and narrowed question concerned the nature of that peculiar subspecies we call "the teenager."

To summarize in a thematic way the issues involved in our discussion of man's nature I will begin with a philosophic cliché. Amongst philosophers it is said that logicians think that metaphysicians are muddle-headed, and metaphysicians think that logicians are simple-minded.

What emerged very interestingly in our group were two extreme views about how to answer the question "Who or what is man?" And from these differing views about how to look for an answer to the question came different answers to the question itself. One method and answer I think I understand; the other I do not understand but I will try to report them both.

The first extreme view that emerged can be stated as a series of

118

simple propositions. (1) There is no knowledge that is not scientific knowledge. (2) Either further or as a consequence, there is no problem that is not a scientific problem. (3) Further, or as a consequence, there is no problem — or no *real* problem — that cannot be exhaustively answered by scientific methods or means. The idea here seems to be that all real or significant human problems will be answered by a better account of what man — as a neuro-physiological or social creature — *is*. Who or what is man? The answer: we should be mindful of the cerebral mechanisms.

I have no doubt that this is one effective means of studying the way man is. If we are interested in scientific facts about human beings, the way to study those facts is scientifically. The trouble with this approach is not that it leaves out the question of what man *ought to be:* such "ought-questions" may have no proper place in a strictly scientific context. The trouble is that holders of this view tend to smuggle into their work contraband concepts of what man ought to be. They bring into their position unexamined value judgments disguised as statements of scientific fact. They may, for instance, slip in value judgments about how children ought to be trained to interpret reality, or about the rightness and goodness or wrongness and badness of various ideological systems that children can be taught.

The trouble is not that these are extra- scientific judgments, but that they tend to be — as we used to say in Oklahoma — "snuck in" — and thus escape critical examination. For that reason this kind of smuggled value judgment is most often naive and crude, and very often a simple-minded restatement of some old philosophic bubble that burst a hundred years ago.

I do not say we should stop making value judgments — that would be an absurd thing to say. My plea is that we recognize value judgments for what they are, and then subject them to severe scrutiny. Such criticism is one of the chief jobs of philosophy. The refusal to use philosophy consciously and knowingly does not lead to no philosophy at all; it leads to bad philosophy.

So much for the one extreme. The contrary extreme — and these extremes are in some ways reactions to each other — counters simple-mindedness with muddle-headedness. It is hard to come to grips with the latter; it is like trying to grasp a jellyfish — which can sting. Rhetorically it seems to rely on mysterious atmospheric effects and playing with loaded words. I suspect that the position really rests on a pair of platitudes and an unargued assumption. The platitudes are that individuals differ from each other and that human beings differ from everything else. These assumptions lead to the conclusion that man as he is cannot be understood in scientific terms.

I think it is correct to say that value questions, questions about what ought to be (unless they are merely questions about means to some already decided end), cannot be answered scientifically. But we here have been given no reason to believe that questions about what is the case, including questions about man, cannot be answered in factual and scientific terms.

Facts and values are related; "is questions" and "ought questions" are related. Just how they are related is a philosophic problem. The problem is not aided by the refusal to recognize that one is doing philosophy or by refusal to do philosophy in a clear-headed, careful, linguistically sober and responsible way. We are all philosophers. Our philosophy will be worse than useless, it will be dangerous, if we abandon standards of good evidence and cogent argument.

The other topic in our first meeting was teenagers — we wondered what their world was like and how it differed from ours. My notion was that this discussion should include the maximum feasible participation of teenagers but we had to manage without that. We all agreed that it was impossible to generalize, which did not even slightly inhibit us when it came to making generalizations. There was some variety of opinion, perhaps reflecting differences of observation. It was very eloquently noted, for instance, that much in teenagers' lives that may appear to us undifferentiated and crude — the example given was rock and roll music — is to the attentive ear various and subtle. It was said that they are better read than we were, that they can and would make their particular sense of life intelligible to us if we would only have the patience to listen and that one of the things they most resent is our uncomprehending impatience. They want our patience and they want our respect.

It was suggested that the reason we are disturbed by the learned among them is that they are asking existential questions while we ask essential questions. Given more time than we now have, it might just be possible to make sense of this suggestion. A credibility gap exists between the middle-aged "us" and the youthful "them." They not only believe that we have failed to make a world as good as the world they could make, which is something young people always believe, but that we are hypocrites. They do not believe us, and believe us least of all when we moralize.

But I think it is fair to say that we ended on a reasonably hopeful note. Changes in style of life we have always had with us and always will. The pace of change is particularly rapid now. This means we have a problem — a problem of understanding between generations — that is new in degree but not new in kind. The ingredients of its solution are what they have always been: knowledge, sensitivity, tact, great patience and love.

With respect to this morning's paper there was agreement on both the desirability and the difficulty of decentralization for government and for industry. The difficulties had to do with personnel, organization, tradition and law. An interesting general difference appeared in this discussion. Some of us were emphasizing the difficulties, others emphasizing our needs or hopes. It was encouraging that no one made the usual moves of taking difficulty as a reason for doing nothing, or of taking hope as an excuse for pretending that there were no difficulties.

CHAPTER 9

Basic Conditions for Tomorrow's World

Barbara Ward

Author, Lecturer, Writer

The chief thing in communication is that the words should continue to have some freshness of meaning. They should continue to penetrate this sort of fuzzy grey substance we call our brains and get down to the imagination to the place where conviction is formed and where action can be generated.

One of the troubles about communicating a great deal is that this coinage of words gets all its lovely shine rubbed off it. We feel we know it all. We've heard everything. Yet we go on thinking we've heard about things long enough, we feel they are old and stale and in any case have been settled or lost their urgency. But this is not the case with our gravest problems. And of all these, there is no sphere in which we so desperately need to keep freshness in communication and ability to make words mean something to mind, heart and will as in the problems of our *international* society. Here, above all, we suffer from the temptation to think we've heard it all before from The Sermon on the Mount onwards, the temptation to feel that everything that can be said about it has been said. We can't resist the feeling that the people who remind us that we could blow up the whole human race are no longer telling us anything valid and fresh. This is the temptation that we're confronted with every day. So please, try and think

This speech, delivered at the Annual Meeting of the Institute of Life Insurance on December 13, 1966, is included herein because of its relevance to the theme of individual responsibility in a changing society.

about the human race as it really is . . . not large and safe and prosperous but precarious and vulnerable and inhabiting a very small planet.

To me one of the great justifications of the space program is its quality to reawaken our imagination. Space expenditures is sometimes, I admit, compared unfavorably with all the things we could do on earth, if we had the same amount of dough. I would say "No" to this criticism for two reasons. The first is the great thrust of human curiosity. This, surely, is one of the strange, strange creatures of man's most valuable and most respectable characteristics. So don't let us quell it. The second reason lies in the quality of human imagination. If we did not now know that a young man can walk round this planet in under two hours, how long would it take us to see our planet as it really is . . . as a neighborhood, as something not much bigger than a village?

Science and technology and our economic system have been building up, web after web after web and link after link, over the last 150 years on this shrinking interdependent planet. Communication can link it instantly . . . through Comsat or Telstar or Early Bird. We may in fact be more closely in touch than in a village. Add the two hour walk and we have the physical nearness we have in a village, the interdependence that we have in a village. This is what we have made . . . a village planet. And I would say, that looking to the future, to the year 2000, there is one issue that transcends all other issues. There are, if you like, subsections A, B and C of the main problem. And that is: in a planet which we've made small and one, can we match our physical unity with the institutions of moral unity . . . of political order, civil responsibility and brotherly compassion.

Without these virtues, society is a rubble. Society is an antheap. Society is merely a conjunction of competing interests which have no means of escaping the rough conflicts which inevitably arrive. And behind these conflicts lies the profoundest of all our unities — and risks, the risk that we could blow ourselves up. Don't let us be like Dr. Strangelove, don't let us live with our bomb and love it. Let us realize that the possibility of nuclear destruction is not a cliché but a *fact*. Let this be a place where the coinage of words is still valid, still rings true and does not suffer from the inflation of repetition which devalues so much of our thinking.

Here is our first priority — to find the civilized institutions needed for a single humanity inhabiting a very small planet. Where do we begin and how do we avoid discouragement? We don't need to do much scanning of the newspapers to see that the institutions, policies and ideas of a civilized order are not exactly springing to life minute by minute as we watch. We live not only on a small planet, but also on a very troubled planet. There is no point in kidding ourselves about our risks. In fact, I feel one of the things we need when we face such facts is that profoundly civic virtue of courage and the ability to believe that our world can continue and that we can work for its good order. Girding ourselves with courage, then, let us ask what are the chief civilizing institutions of human society? There are, of course, a great many and since our time is short, I propose to pick out only three.

Chief Civilizing Institutions

The first is composed of the rule of law and the impartial policing system that goes with it. The second is the principle of "the general welfare." And the third is that indefinable thing which, I am told, we mustn't call "consensus." Yet the word does express the desire of people to live together as a community in spite of all their differences. Perhaps a better word would be a "civic philosophy." It is the same kind of overall readiness to accept that we are humans and have to live together that we do achieve inside our local domestic societies. It is neighbourliness with all its patience and restraint . . . but on a planetary scale.

If you say that it's impossible to put these three great civilizing institutions or ideas to work in the world at large, I would quickly point out that we have, in human history, achieved this degree of civil order over very, very wide areas. The great free republic of the United States is continent-wide. If you had told Aristotle or Plato that a law-abiding republic could have ever been larger than a city-state, they would just have had a good laugh.

Again for over 2000 years China, under largely bureaucratic government underpinned an orderly civilized community with the longest continuous history — so far — in the human record. And this system covered a quarter of humanity. The Chinese are always a quarter of the human race. Whatever you do, the rest of mankind can increase and increase — no good, Chinese have always been a quarter of the human race and by golly they still are.

So do not let us say planetary scale makes civilized institutions impossible. A quarter of the human race have realized some of the orderly institutions of a civilized community and you cannot say that a thing done by a quarter is absolutely inconceivable for the whole. In other words, yes, it can be done.

A Rule of Law

But is it being done? Where are we now? Let us begin with a rule of law. We have made one gesture to reality. We have said we need a United Nations. True, we then rapidly retreat and say that the United Nations mustn't, of course, touch our sovereignty. There must be no question of interfering with the great power to veto and so on. Yet the new effort has at least outlasted the old League of Nations. We still have a working institution which expresses a certain timid political will to solve disputes peacefully. Through it, we have made some experiments in orderly peace-keeping. We have had some supervision of the conflict in Kashmir and one result was that when the Kashmir War broke out last year, it was stopped in its tracks.

We've had some control in the Middle East. We have still a measure of supervision in Cyprus. We made an experiment in the Congo which, though not perfect, might have been much worse. All these things are facts. Like a bather putting a toe in very cold water, the world has at least put the toe into the icy waters of post-national policing.

Two other conflicts which are much in our minds now, also suggest the new concepts of the idea of a rule of law with impartial police power. The Korean War came to an end in a negotiated armistice under U.N. auspices. And now the search is on for a similar end to the Viet Nam War.

You must forgive an outsider coming in talking about this war. The British, it is true, have had a little experience in this kind of fighting. The Indian frontiers and recently Malaya offered the same type of long-drawn inconclusive struggle. As you know, the Viet Nam War is criticized on the one hand by those who say, it's the wrong war in the wrong place and shouldn't be fought at all. It's

125

also criticized very strenuously by those who say: blow everything up and finish it off fast. I would like to put to you a third outlook — the possibility that this war — puzzling as it is, is an attempt to reach out beyond the old concept of victory and defeat and punishing the enemy — which leaves all the wounds of conflict to fester. This war is much nearer to a policing operation. What is at stake is the right of people in South Viet Nam to decide their political future without having their throats cut. This is a principle of great importance. The idea that people should not be coerced by violence in deciding their political future, is one surely that should be policed. And if at the time, there is no international agency to undertake that policing, then it's valid that a great power like America and its allies should do it instead. This is the acceptable argument for American involvement. But it also sets the limits of the operation.

Their forces in Viet Nam, being police forces, are not out for total victory. They are not out to smash North Viet Nam or punish the Chinese. They are conducting a limited operation . . . to defend the right of the peoples of South Viet Nam to decide their own future. What implications does this have for the actual operations? Now I don't want to be an arm chair strategist. I think nothing is more tiresome than the number of people who put on the general's hats . . . at the drop of one of those general's hats.

What I'm going to suggest now, I put to you not because I am a strategist . . . God knows I'm not . . . but simply because I am a European. And along with a lot of my fellow Europeans, I've lived through a concrete historical experience which I think has some relevance to the Vietnamese crisis.

The first point is I have been bombed fairly steadily for four years. A lot of my fellow Europeans were bombed even more steadily for four years and I have to tell you, ladies and gentlemen, that being bombed — short of actually being dead yourself — doesn't stop very much. The postwar surveys of bomb damage showed that war-making capacity had not been decisively interrupted. The concept of bringing wars to an end by massive bombing was tried out but it did not work. The technique of mass bombing — which I think takes us beyond policing and towards concepts of violence, even revenge — is counter-productive.

But another experience in Europe is possibly revelant. It's a sad

126

one but one cannot deny its effectiveness. And it is quite simply the Iron Curtain. The Communists sealed themselves off because they knew otherwise a large part of the population of Eastern Europe would move West — which would have been awkward from the Marxist standpoint. But a combination of triple barbed wire, mine fields, watchtowers, with overlapping fields of machine gun fire — all this effectively sees that people don't get through. Here in the concept of the shield, we have perhaps the technological possibility of achieving a controlled and restricted field of combat, a strategy which does not seek "total victory," but continues a policing operation and gives that essentially defensive and limited weapon — a shield behind which the South Vietnamese can return to a political process with debates instead of cut throats and ballots not bullets.

I myself would like to see that political process under international supervision. And if we could combine this possibility of a shield to prevent external infiltration with internal consultation under U.N. supervision, perhaps we might begin to have a technique for dealing with the kind of civil disturbance we're most likely to have — which is the so-called war of national liberation.

I suggest this not, Heaven knows, because I'm a strategist, but because there is surely relevance in Europe's recent vivid experience — of failure on the one hand through heavy bombing, of considerable success — also — through the other . . . through the shield, the wall, the preventive barrier. Behind such a shield, might not Viet Nam appear more clearly what it essentially is — a limited police operation — one which can be seen to serve the purpose of building a world where ultimately politics will be a matter not of violence but of choice? Because this is the essence of civil order.

If as a result of a limited operation in Viet Nam mankind can evolve techniques under international supervision for dealing with guerilla wars, then we can edge back a little from that terrible height that overlooks Armageddon — and possibly the end of our human experiment.

The General Welfare

Now we must turn to the second principle of civil order — the general welfare. Societies are peaceful societies if people have hope. We should never forget that when Hitler came to power in Germany there was a quarter of the work force unemployed. He took over violent control at a time of the utmost misery. Can we think today that this narrow planet with its enormous degree of economic interdependence can survive as a relatively peaceful world, and grow into a more cooperative world, if two thirds of its people live in conditions of such misery that like the Germans in 1930 they simply lose hope? Is not a whole series of violent conflicts and counter-conflicts shaking the earth like Viet Nam, a more likely outcome?

This is where we are. In a sense, we in the Atlantic world are rather like the very rich minority in the 19th Century in Britain or the United States. Wealth was being created by the vast productivity of the new industrial system. But it flowed into very few hands. Our society had not then learned by a whole series of policies, public and private, to extend wealth and purchasing power to the mass of the people and make the mass market the basis of the free enterprise economy. Today, we are in a comparable position in the world at large. We in the West, who control 80 percent of the world's wealth, trade and investment, make up no more than 16 percent of the people. We are collective Rockefellers, Jay Goulds and Harrimans and Vanderbilts.

Now if we look at the social history, of that time, we find that there was a continuous surging undercurrent of resentment and of pressure . . . political pressure, because of this enormous maldistribution of wealth. What is more, that maldistribution was ultimately bad for business as well because if you're going to produce things you've got to see them somewhere. And if the market is, in fact, not expanding, the incredible productivity of the new machines comes slap up against the inadequacy of the market. One of the chief reasons for the recurrent depressions of the 19th and 20th Century, culminating in the greatest Depression of them all in 1929 . . . which tipped us back into war . . . was . . . as we now see with hindsight . . . the inadequacy of the market to expand and meet the full enormous flood of productivity from the new enterprises and the new machines. At the time they were called crises of over-production. They might as well have been called crises of under-consumption.

The process of economic growth and productivity has not

stopped. The goods that can pour out of this economy continue to be ever more astonishing and are certain to grow more so. We have integrated into the productive process a new factor of growth in the shape of systematic research. Since research proceeds from the known to the unknown, the more you know, the more rapidly you move forward. So now, photographing the dark side of the moon is just child's play. And it is only a start. As somebody said, if they can lick the plumbing problems inside that space capsule, we can look forward to cities without drains. All sorts of fallouts from the new research and technology lie ahead. A whole new field of productivity is about to surge up about us. In fact I was recently out at Detroit to see the Enrico Fermi breeder-reactor. I confessed to the experts that I did not fully understand how it is that apparently more energy is produced than is actually used .It seemed to me unlikely. They said: "well, think of some well-known families around the place and you'll see that two can produce ten." In other words, the breeder-reactor is a faithful representative of the old ideal of the Victorian family — the outcome is not babies but plutonium. But energy on this scale is one more example of the incredible new reaches of productivity that lie ahead. It follows that we shall have to be just as inventive and just as resourceful in thinking of ways in which we can expand our markets.

This is why I get terribly impatient when people talk about economic assistance and development strategy for two-thirds of the human race as though we were being kind and generous. On the contrary, it is one of the soundest principles of self-interest to see that as the enormous productive powers of Japan, Russia, Europe and America go up and up and up that . . . for Heaven's sake . . . we pull up a market behind them. No doubt we can still increase demand inside the developed world. But on a comparable scale there may come a day, ladies and gentlemen, when you've got color TV in the living room and in the dining room and in the bathroom and in three of the bedrooms, and also down by the pool. Then you won't be able to use another color TV.

And so it is with the fourth car, the third swimming pool, the second house. There are limits. Incidentally, we are already within sight of the limit in food, with grave difficulties for farmers all around the world. The stomach is technologically incompetent in that you can't stretch it — and nothing is more technologically incompetent, I may say, than the fashion conscious female figure, because we're *determined* not to stretch it. What has happened in the field of food, where we, the rich nations, are reaching the outer limits of possible consumption, can happen in other fields.

We might then, in the last decades of this century, face a position in which on the one hand, enormous increases in productivity continue to surge forward but there is a desperate failure of the market of humanity, the market of mankind, to expand in the same proportion. So for me economic assistance — to which I am absolutely, firmly convinced we ought to devote at least one percent of our national income — is in fact part of a development strategy to make sure that the market of humanity keep pace with the productivity of humanity. If the balance is lost, we could confront the kind of contradiction and the kind of trouble which in 1929 plunged our developed world into a disaster from which we didn't emerge except at the end of a long war. And we couldn't afford to have that kind of war again. We've invented the atom bomb since. Therefore we have to avoid that kind of risk.

Now I believe that as a result of fifteen years of conducting world development — through economic assistance, through the work of the World Bank, through the International Development Association, through all the various programs of development at the U.N. — we know an awful lot more about how to combine public and private enterprise in this field. We have learned some of the basic principles of a growth strategy designed to pull the developing two-thirds of humanity across the threshold into the modern economy. Because of this, I think it is nothing short of tragic that so many people today on both sides of the Atlantic know so little about these programs — their expansion, their strategy, their success — that they are content to listen without protest or rebuttal when people talk nonsense — utter nonsense — about "operation Rathole."

Now, for Heaven's sake, how many people know that since 1960, the Pakistanis, by a combination made up of 80 percent of their own efforts and about 10 percent of public help and 10 percent of foreign investment have, in fact, quadrupled their output of food and increased their industrial growth by something like 16 percent a year. How many people know that that apparently hopeless case, South Korea, has been growing by about 10 percent a year since the early sixties? This isn't failure. True, both countries are at the beginning of the full process of modernization — and we know in the Western World that it takes about 50 to 60 years to become a fully developed modern economy. But to go and stop these programs just when we are beginning to know so much more about the techniques of growth, to miss out on our own fundamental interest in creating a world-wide market adequate to deal with the technologies we are expanding all the time, this seems to me a monumental folly to which I could put a name — but perhaps I had better not.

A Reasonable Consensus

It is folly, too, in relation to the third of our pre-conditions of civilized living — a reasonable consensus. We shall achieve no philosophy for human society if people despair. Take one of the most basic reasons for despair . . . starvation. We know already that there will be another billion people by 1980 and we know that if they are to be fed, there has to be something like a 25 percent increase in food production over that period. This we know now. But we are not behaving like rational human beings because we're not connecting our knowledge with our policy. Birth-control, incidentally, is no alibi. It will come. If cultures as diverse as Western Europe and Japan can stabilize their populations, so can and will others. But the billion extra will be there by 1980 in any case.

Meanwhile we hang around and give increased food production neither urgency nor thought nor dedication. This is the very recipe for mass despair and with all due respect to Mr. Mao Tse-tung, I think despair, not revolutionary ideology is the risk of the future. I think we are seeing the end of the violent ideological division. Take the Russians. Their new dedication to the profit motive and the market system must give us all a little underground pleasure, I must say. The idea of Mr. Henry Luce's group of businessmen being lectured on the profit motive by a Communist economist in Prague has given me infinite and considerable joy. It is often wonderful, the prophetic zeal with which people come on to a new idea.

But what is fascinating is to see the Russians reaching out to what you can only call pragmatism, leaving Marxism as a set of beliefs to which lip service is paid but does not affect "real" politics — perhaps the way in which Westerners tend to treat *their* religion.

What Soviet society as a whole looks for is much more a pragmatic understanding of how the world works, of what is going on and combines it with a passionate desire to get out and see. One of the reasons why all the young people of Eastern Europe and Russia pine for foreign travel is because of this reach, this desire to get out into a wider human experience. And although I am not a Mao Tse-tung watcher — or whatever I ought to be — I suspect that one of the reasons he is having so much trouble with his Communists is the tendency of the Chinese people, too, to become bourgeois. He is using the wildness of extreme youth to persuade people that they must still be puritans, still accept the prophets of the true religion. So even the trouble in China suggests that we're living in the twilight of the great ideological divisions.

But this fact is not of itself wholly reassuring. We might also be living in the unhappy dawn of an age of despair. If you can be a Communist, you still hope about the future, you still believe in man's ability to do something about his problem. You still have a picture of the kingdom of Heaven on earth, you still have some idea that mankind is in control of his destiny.

Might we not, if we allow the world-wide drift to poverty and starvation to continue, might we not wake up to the day when people no longer even believe in humanity? When they no longer have any confidence in the human experiment? When they revert to the apathy and despair which is the ultimate destruction of civil order? There are signs enough in the art and literature and student movements in our Western World to suggest an underlying mood of sick, black despair, a nihilist rejection of society itself. Might we not see all round the world, that final loss of confidence in man himself without which the human system — which demands intense courage, immense fortitude and immense faith — cannot continue?

It may be all too easy to confront the complexity of the modern world — so productive in its technology, so heartless in its faith — and simply give up. The growth of our cities, the scale of our apparatus — political or industrial — the feeling of being dwarfed, the feeling that "things are in the saddle" and man has lost control — all these are possible reactions to our plight today and could be the death of the human experiment almost as certainly as the bomb itself.

So I feel that ultimately the challenge before the Western World now is the profoundest of all — the challenge of hope. How are we to restore the sense that this whole apparatus still makes sense? And the obvious answer is to set to work to see that it does. We have wealth enough to act, we have the technology at our elbows, we have the trained minds, the research, the ability to make our vast resources the servant of a genuine world-wide strategy of growth and modernization. If we were going forward confidently not to expand indefinitely our instruments of destruction but to devise a strategy to lead mankind not, Heaven knows, to the promised land. But to a land which makes sense in terms of opportunity, of education for its children, of food for all its citizens and work and shelter, which gives them above all hope that tomorrow can be better for their children than today and that their work and effort will help in the task.

If we were using our resources in this way, the world would avoid despair. I think we could restore to our human society the profound virtue of hope. I don't know that any other civilization has quite produced it. If you look at the other cultures, you will find that again and again, they have been cultures of resignation. They have believed in "the melancholy wheel," in tomorrows that would be no better than yesterday and in a wisdom that taught one to conform and keep quiet. And suddenly into the human experiment, erupted this tremendous force of the Jewish and the Christian ideal which looks to a millennium, believes in the future, thinks progress possible and believes that man has the highest of all attributes, which is to be the co-creator of his world with God himself. This has been the earth-shaking vision which has sent us forward with the energy we still see and which can still work with us, if we do not lose faith.

And so I would say to this great Institute which carries, after all, so much of the hopes and savings of individual families, which is so bound up in the possibility of a decent future, help us to hope, help us to keep faith. Let the human experiment feel that it can succeed.

Participants in the Arden House Conference on "Today's Changing Society — A Challenge to Individual Identity"

Dr. Harry Alpert
Dean of Faculties
University of Oregon

Dr. Chester M. Alter
Chancellor
University of Denver

Mr. Milton Amsel
Director, Press Bureau
Institute of Life Insurance

Mr. Orville E. Beal
President
The Prudential Insurance
  Company of America

Dr. Lawrence S. Bee
Department of Sociology
The University of Kansas

Dr. Myron B. Bloy, Jr.
Executive Director
The Church Society for
  College Work

Dr. Arthur W. Brown
President
Adelphi University

Dr. Courtney C. Brown
Dean, Graduate School of Business
Columbia University

Mr. T. S. Burnett
Chairman
Pacific Mutual Life Insurance
  Company

Dr. Jerome B. Cohen
Department of Economics
Bernard M. Baruch School of
  Business and Public Administration
The City University of New York

Dr. Bingham Dai
Department of Psychiatry
Duke University Medical Center

Mr. Arthur C. Daniels
Vice President
Institute of Life Insurance

Dr. José M. R. Delgado
Department of Psychiatry
Yale University School of
  Medicine

Mr. Robert E. Dineen
President
The Northwestern Mutual Life
  Insurance Company

Mr. Byron K. Elliott
Chairman of the Board
John Hancock Mutual Life Insurance
  Company

Dr. William M. Evan
Department of Sociology
Wharton School of Finance and
  Commerce
University of Pennsylvania

Dr. John R. Everett
President
The New School for Social Research

Mr. E. J. Faulkner
President
Woodmen Accident and Life
  Company

Mr. Gilbert W. Fitzhugh
Chairman of the Board
Metropolitan Life Insurance
  Company

134

Dr. Davis W. Gregg
President
American College of Life
 Underwriters

Dr. Serge Grosset
School of Business Administration
Duquesne University

Dr. Sidney Hook
Department of Philosophy
New York University

Mr. Walter H. Huehl
President
Indianapolis Life Insurance
 Company

Mr. Burkett W. Huey
Executive Vice President
 and Managing Director
Life Insurance Agency Management
 Association

Mr. J. McCall Hughes
Executive Vice President
The Mutual Life Insurance
 Company of New York

Mr. Roger Hull
President
The Mutual Life Insurance Company
 of New York

Mr. Raymond C. Johnson
Executive Vice President
New York Life Insurance Company

Dr. John A. Larson
Senior Staff Member
Advanced Study Program
The Brookings Institution

Dr. C. Douglas McGee
Department of Philosophy
Bowdoin College

Dr. Thomas P. McTighe
Department of Philosophy
Georgetown University

Dr. John J. Meng
Executive Vice President
Fordham University

Dr. Harlan B. Miller
Director, Educational Division
Institute of Life Insurance

Mr. John H. Miller
President-Elect
American Academy of Actuaries

Mr. Howard A. Moreen
Senior Vice President
Aetna Life Insurance Company

Mr. Blake T. Newton, Jr.
President
Institute of Life Insurance

Mr. James F. Oates, Jr.
Chairman of the Board
The Equitable Life Assurance
 Society of the United States

Mr. William K. Paynter
Vice President
Institute of Life Insurance

Dr. Paul J. Piccard
Department of Government
The Florida State University

Mr. John S. Pillsbury, Jr.
President
Northwestern National Life
 Insurance Company

Dr. Daniel O. Price
Director, Institute for Research in
 Social Science
Department of Sociology
The University of Texas

Dr. John W. Riley, Jr.
Vice President and Director of
 Social Research
The Equitable Life Assurance
 Society of the United States

Mr. W. Lee Shield
Executive Vice President
American Life Convention

Mr. Hoke S. Simpson
Director of Executive Programs
Graduate School of Business
Columbia University

135

Mr. Armand Stalnaker
Executive Vice President
General American Life Insurance
  Company

Dr. Frederick F. Stephan
Department of Sociology
Princeton University

Mr. Lyndes B. Stone
President
Phoenix Mutual Life Insurance
  Company

Mr. Eugene M. Thoré
President
Life Insurance Association of
  America

Mr. John A. Tuck
Managing Director
The Canadian Life Insurance
  Association

Dr. Barry Ulanov
Department of English Literature
Barnard College

Mr. Henry C. Unruh
Vice President and Chief Actuary
Provident Life and Accident
  Insurance Company

Mr. Travis T. Wallace
Chairman of the Board
Great American Reserve Insurance
  Company

Dr. Clarence C. Walton
Dean, School of General Studies
Columbia University

Dr. Vincent H. Whitney
Chairman, Department of
  Sociology
Wharton School of Finance and
  Commerce
University of Pennsylvania

Dr. James W. Wiggins
Associate Dean, College of Arts
  and Sciences
Converse College

Mr. Dan C. Williams
President
Southland Life Insurance Company

Dr. Willis J. Winn
Dean, Wharton School of Finance
  and Commerce
University of Pennsylvania

Dr. Leonard N. Wolf
Department of Biology
University of Scranton

Dr. Harry Woolf
Chairman
Department of the History of Science
The Johns Hopkins University